No 1 Hits *for* BUSKERS

ısive distributors:
c Sales Limited
5 Berners Street,
onW1T 3LJ, England.
ic Sales Pty Limited 20
lution Drive, Caringbah,
/ 2229,Australia.

er No.AM956747
978-0-7119-7800-3

pilation by Pete Evans

t cover design by Chloë Alexander

ed in the EU

r Guarantee of Quality
ıblishers, we strive to produce every book to the highest commercial
lards.The book has been carefully designed to minimise awkward page
s and to make playing from it a real pleasure. Particular care has been given
ecifying acid-free, neutral-sized paper made from pulps which have not
elemental chlorine bleached.This pulp is from farmed sustainable forests
was produced with special regard for the environment.Throughout, the
ing and binding have been planned to ensure a sturdy, attractive publication
h should give years of enjoyment. If your copy fails to meet our high
lards, please inform us and we will gladly replace it.

ı.musicsales.com

WISE PUBLICATIONS
PART OF THE MUSIC SALES GROUP
NDON / NEW YORK / PARIS / SYDNEY / COPENHAGEN /
BERLIN / MADRID / HONG KONG / TOKYO

1

And I Love Her

Words & Music by John Lennon & Paul McCartney

Slowly and gently
Fm
Cm
Fm
I give her all my love,
She gives me ev'-ry - thing,
Bright are the stars that shine,
That's all I
And ten - der -
Dark is the

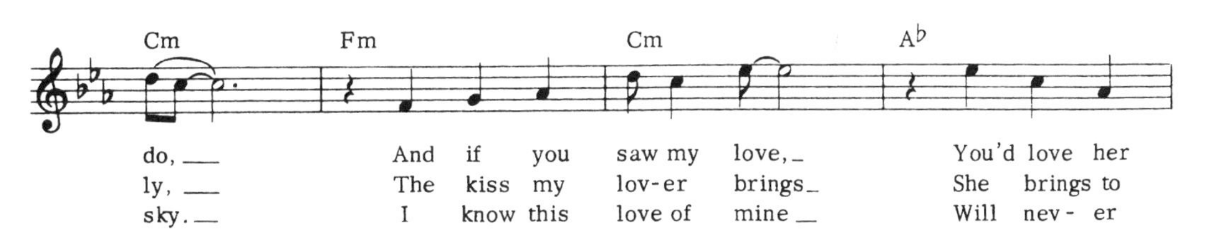
Cm
Fm
Cm
A♭
do,
ly,
sky.
And if you saw my love,
The kiss my lov-er brings
I know this love of mine
You'd love her
She brings to
Will nev- er

B♭7
E♭
To Coda
1
2
Cm
too. I love her.
me, And I love her.
die, And I love her.
A love like ours

B♭
Cm
Gm
Cm
could nev-er die.
As long as I

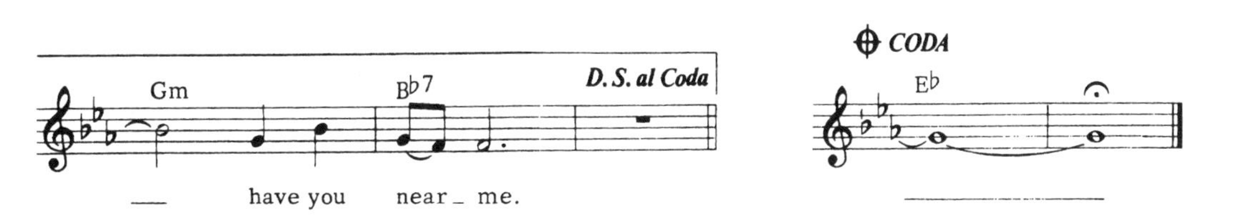
Gm
B♭7
D.S. al Coda
have you near me.
CODA
E♭

2

Annie's Song

Words & Music by John Denver

Moderately
Dsus4 G A Bm G
You fill up my sen - ses like a night in the
des - ert, like a sleep-y blue
D D/C♯ D/B D/A G
for - est, Like the moun-tains in spring -
o - cean, You fill up my sen -
F♯m Em 1 G A7
-time, like a walk in the rain.
-ses, come
2 A7 D Dsus4
Like a storm in the fill me a - gain.
D Dsus4 G A Bm
Come let me love you, let me
sen - ses, like a

G D D/C♯ D/B D/A
give my life to you, Let me drown in your
night in a for - est, Like the moun-tains in
G F♯m Em G A7
laugh - ter, let me die in your arms.
spring - time, like a walk in the rain.
G A Bm
Let me lay down be - side you, let me
Like a storm in the des - ert, like a
G D D/C♯ D/B D/A
al - ways be with you, Come let me
sleep - y blue o - cean, You fill up my
G F♯m Em A7 1 D
love you, come love me a - gain.
sen - ses, come fill me a-
Dsus4 D Dsus4 2 D Dsus4
You fill up my - gain.
D Dsus4 D Dsus4 D

3

BRIDGE OVER TROUBLED WATER

Words & Music by Paul Simon

Quasi Spiritual
C
F
C
When you're wea - ry feel - in' small,
down and out on the street,
F
C
F
When tears are in your eyes, I'll
When eve - ning falls so hard, I'll
C / F / C / F / C
dry them all,
com-fort you,
I'm on your
I'll take your
G
G7
C
3
side, Oh, when times get rough,
part. Oh, when dark - ness comes,
C7
F
D
G
C7
And friends just can't be found,
And pain is all a - round,
Like a
F / /
F#o
C
A7sus
A7
F
E
Bridge o - ver trou - bled wa - ter, I will lay me

Am
C7
F
F♯o
1
C
A7sus
A7
down, Like a Bridge o - ver trou- bled wat -er,
F
G7sus
G7
C
F
I will lay me down.
C
F
C
F
2
C
Am
F
E
When you're trou - bled wat - er, I will ease your
Am
C7
F
D7
C
Am
mind, Like a Bridge o - ver trou - bled wat - er,
F
E
Am
Am7
D9
I will ease your mind.
C
F
Fm
C

4
CLAUDETTE

Words & Music by Roy Orbison

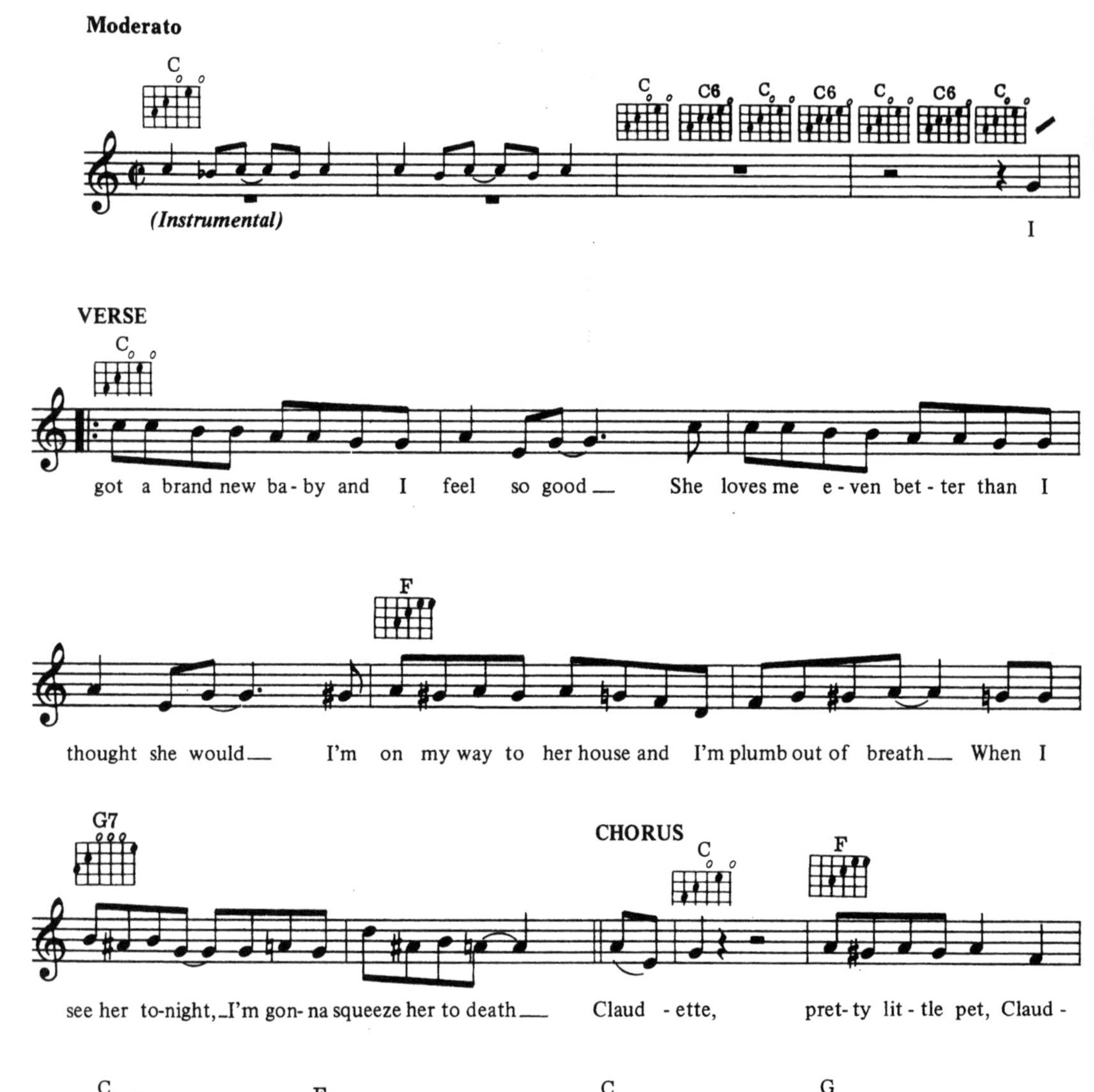
Moderato
C
C C6 C C6 C C6 C
(Instrumental)
I
VERSE
C
got a brand new ba-by and I feel so good__ She loves me e-ven bet-ter than I
F
thought she would__ I'm on my way to her house and I'm plumb out of breath__ When I
G7
CHORUS
C
F
see her to-night,_I'm gon-na squeeze her to death__ Claud - ette, pret-ty lit-tle pet, Claud -
C
F
C
G
- ette Nev-er makes me fret, Claud - ette Well she's the great-est lit-tle girl that

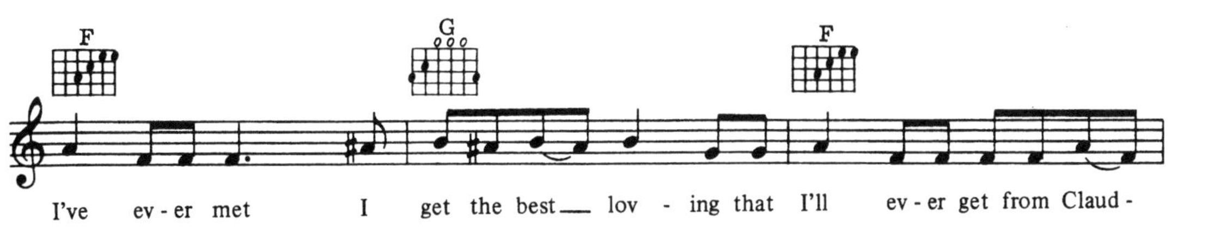
F
G
F
I've ev - er met I get the best lov - ing that I'll ev - er get from Claud -

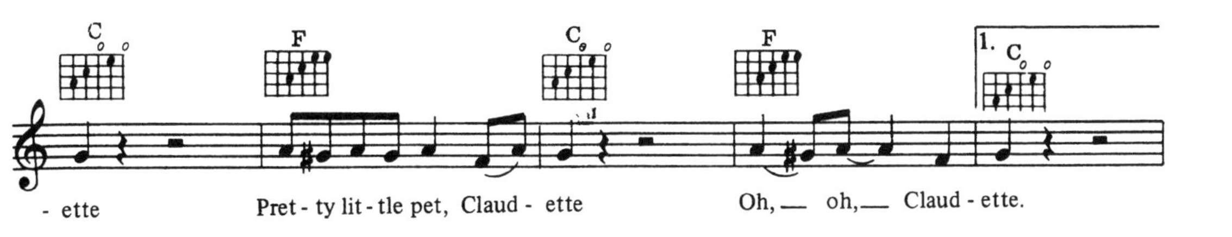
C
F
C
F
1. C
- ette Pret - ty lit - tle pet, Claud - ette Oh, oh, Claud - ette.

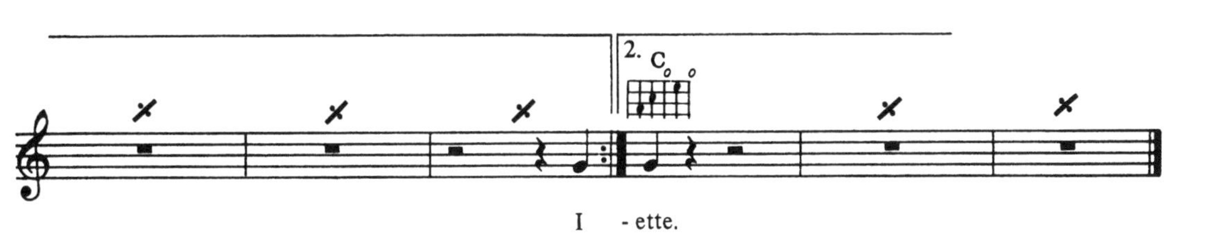
2. C
I - ette.

2. Well, I'm a lucky man, my baby treats me right
   She's gonna let me hug and kiss and hold her tight
   When the date is over and we're at her front door
   When I kiss her goodnight, I holler, 'More, more, more'

3. When me and my new baby have a date or three
   I'm gonna ask her if she'll marry me
   I'm gonna be so happy for the rest of my life
   When my brand new baby is my brand new wife.

Do You Really Want To Hurt Me

Words & Music by George O'Dowd, Jonathan Moss, Roy Hay & Michael Craig

G
Bm7/F♯
Em
Give me time to re - a - lise my crime,
let me love and steal.
I have danced in - side your eyes,
How can I be - real.
Bm
C
Am
1. Do you real - ly want to hurt me,
2. In my heart the fire is burn - ing,
Do you real - ly want to make me cry.
Choose my col - our find a star.
Pre - cious kiss - es words that burn me,
Pre - cious peo - ple al - ways tell me,

Bm
1
2
Lov-ers nev-er ask — you why.
That's a step a step too far. —
CHORUS
G Bm Em G Bm Em
Do you real-ly want to hurt me, — Do you real-ly want to make me — cry. —
C G Am Bm
To Coda
Do you real-ly want to hurt me, — Do you real-ly want to make me — cry. —
B♭ A♭ Gm
VERSE 2.
Words are few I have spoken, I could waste a thousand years,
Wrapped in sorrow, words are token, come inside and catch my tears.
You've been talking but believe me, if it's true you do not know,
This boy loves without a reason, I'm prepared to let you go.
C D C
If it's — love — you — want from — me — then take it — a-way,
D C D
Ev - 'ry - thing's — not — what you — see. — It's
C D
D.%. al Coda
CODA B♭
o - ver — a- gain. —

6
DON'T CRY FOR ME ARGENTINA

Music by Andrew Lloyd Webber
Words by Tim Rice

Slowly
C
F/C
1. It won't be ea-sy, you'll think it strange, When I try to ex-plain how I
G7/C
C
feel, That I still need your love af-ter all that I've done: You won't be-
Am/C
D
D/C
-lieve me, All you will see is a girl you once knew, Al-though she's dressed up to the
G/B
D7
G
C
nines at six-es and sev-ens with you.
2. I had to let it
3. And as for
F/C
G7/C
hap-pen, I had to change; Could-n't stay all my life down at heel: Look-ing
for-tune, and as for fame; I nev-er in-vi-ted them in: Though it
C
Cmaj7
out of the win-dow, stay-ing out of the sun. So I chose
seemed to the world they were all I de-sired. They are il-

Am/C
D7
free - dom, Run-ning a - round try - ing ev - 'ry - thing new, but
-lu - sions, they're not the sol - u - tions they prom-ised to be, the
D/C
G/B
D7
no - thing im-pressed me at all, I nev - er ex - pect - ed it
an - swer was here all the time, I love you, and hope you love
G
CHORUS
C
to.
me,
Don't cry for me Ar - gen - ti - na, the
G
truth is I nev - er left you: All through my wild days, my mad ex-
Am
Cmaj7
Fmaj7
To Coda
-ist-ence, I kept my prom-ise, Don't keep your dis- tance.
1
F6
F
2
Fmaj7
Have I said too much? there's no-thing more I can think of to
Em7
Fmaj7
say to you. But all you have to do is
C
D.S. al Coda
CODA
Fmaj7
F6
C
look at me to know that ev - 'ry word is true.

Don't Give Up On Us

Words & Music by Tony Macaulay

Moderato
A
Amaj7
Don't give up on us ba— by Don't make the
up on us ba— by We're still worth
up on us ba— by Lord knows we've

D
E
C#m
F#m
wrong seem right, The fu-ture is-n't just one— night
one more try, And though we put a last one — by
come this far, Why can't we stay the way we — are

D
A
1
D
It's writ-ten in the moon light— and paint-ed on the stars-
Just for a rain - y even ing —
The an-gel and the dream er —

A
Bm7
D
2
D
— We can't change ours,
Don't give
when may-be stars are
when someone plays a

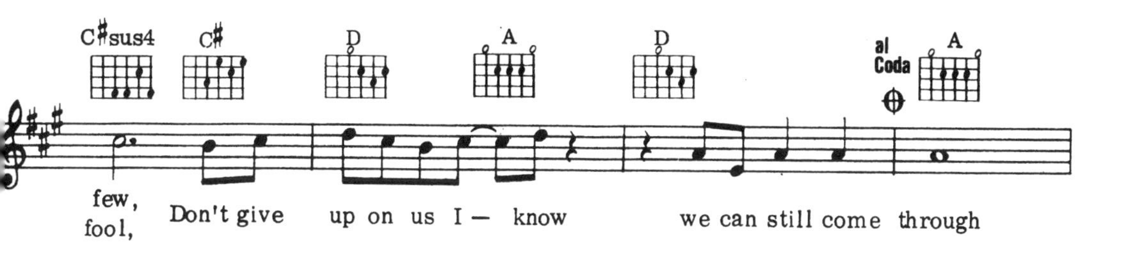
C♯sus4
C♯
D
A
D
al Coda
A
few,
fool,
Don't give
up on us I — know
we can still come through

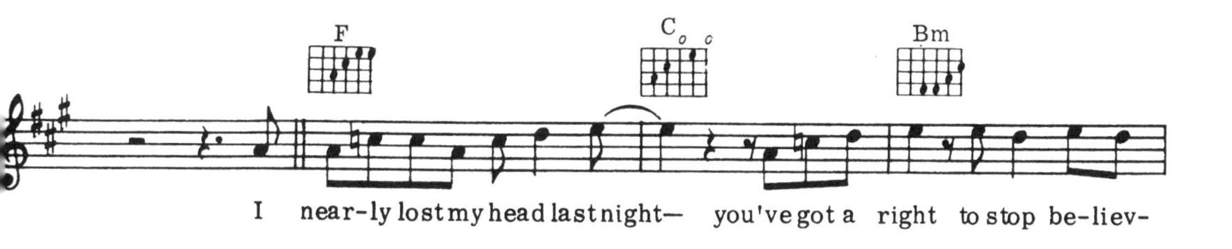
F
C
Bm
I near-ly lost my head last night— you've got a right to stop be-liev-

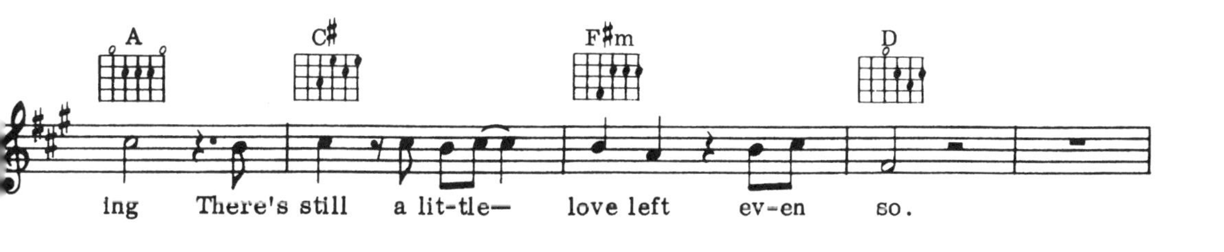
A
C♯
F♯m
D
ing There's still a lit-tle— love left ev-en so.

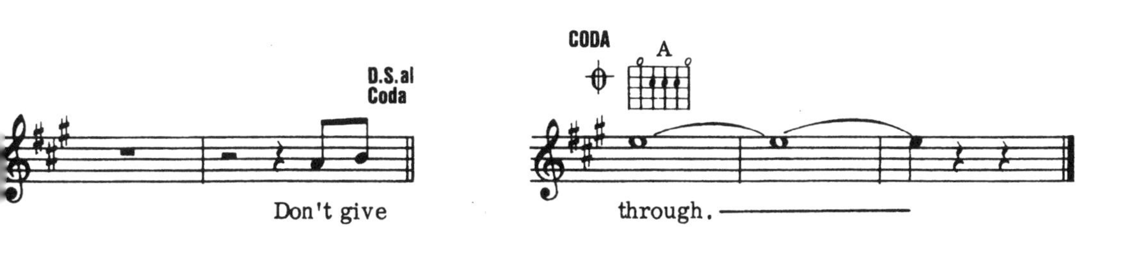
D.S. al Coda
CODA
A
Don't give
through. ——

8

Careless Whisper

Words & Music by George Michael & Andrew Ridgeley

Slow ballad
Dm
Gm7
3 fr.
Am7
B♭maj7
Am7
Dm
Gm7
3 fr.
Am7
B♭maj7
Am7
Dm7
Gm7
3 fr.
Am7
B♭maj7
1. I feel so unsure as I take your hand and lead you
2. Time can never mend the careless whisper
(See lyric 3)

Am7
Dm7
to the dance floor; as the mu - sic dies
of a good friend; to the heart and mind
Gm7
3 fr.
Am7
B♭maj7
some - thing in your eyes calls to mind a sil - ver screen and
ig - nor - ance is kind there's no com - fort in the truth,
Am7
Dm
you're its sad good - bye. I'm ne - ver gon - na dance a - gain,
pain is all you'll find.
Gm7
3 fr.
Am7
B♭maj7
guil - ty feet have got no rhy - thm, though it's ea - sy to pre - tend, I
Am7
Dm
know you're not a fool. I should have known bet - ter than to cheat a friend, and
Gm7
3 fr.
Am7
B♭maj7
To Coda
waste a chance that I've been gi - ven, so I'm ne - ver gon - na dance a - gain the

1.
Am7
Dm
Gm7
3 fr.
Am7
way I dance _ with you. ___
B♭maj7
Am7
2.
D.S. al Cod
Am7
way I dance _ with you, oh. ___

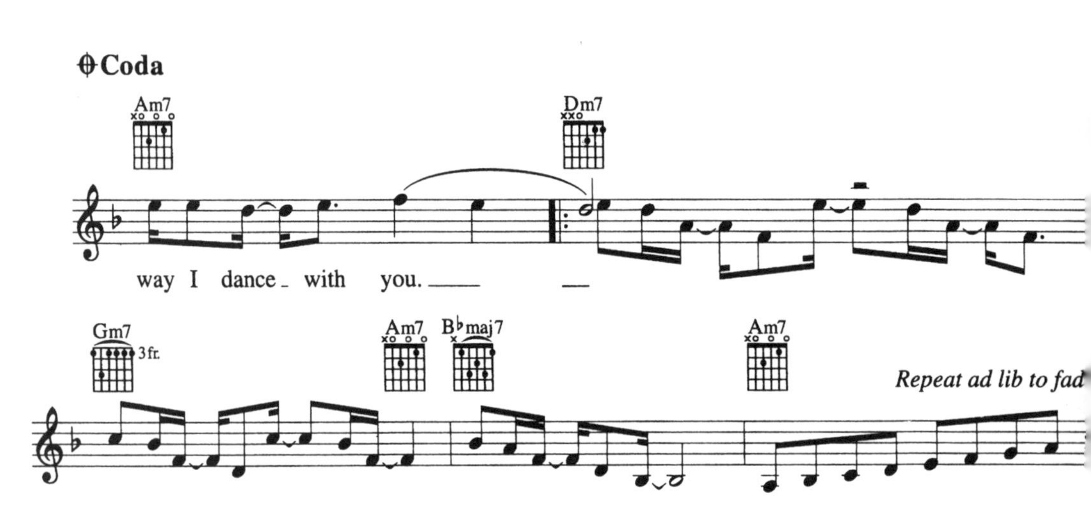
Coda
Am7
Dm7
way I dance _ with you. ___ ___
Gm7
3 fr.
Am7
B♭maj7
Am7
Repeat ad lib to fad

3. Tonight the music seems so loud,
I wish that we could lose this crowd,
Maybe it's better this way,
If we'd hurt each other with the things we want to say.
We could have been so good together,
We could have lived this dance forever,
But now who's gonna dance with me.
Please dance.

Don't Go Breaking My Heart

Words & Music by Ann Orson & Carte Blanche

Moderately
F
Bb/F
F
Don't go break-ing my heart
I could-n't if I tried.
And no - bo -dy told us
'Cause no-bo - dy showed us.
Bb
F
C/Bb
Bb
G7/B
Oh, hon-ey if I get rest - less
And now it's up to us babe,
F/C
Bb
F
Bb
F
Bb
C7
Ba -by you're not that kind.
Oh, I think we can make it.
F
Bb/F
F
Don't go break-ing my heart,
So don't mis-un - der - stand me,
You take the weight off me.
You put the light in my life.
Bb
F
Bb
G7
Oh hon - ey when you knock at my door,
Oh you put the spark to the flame,

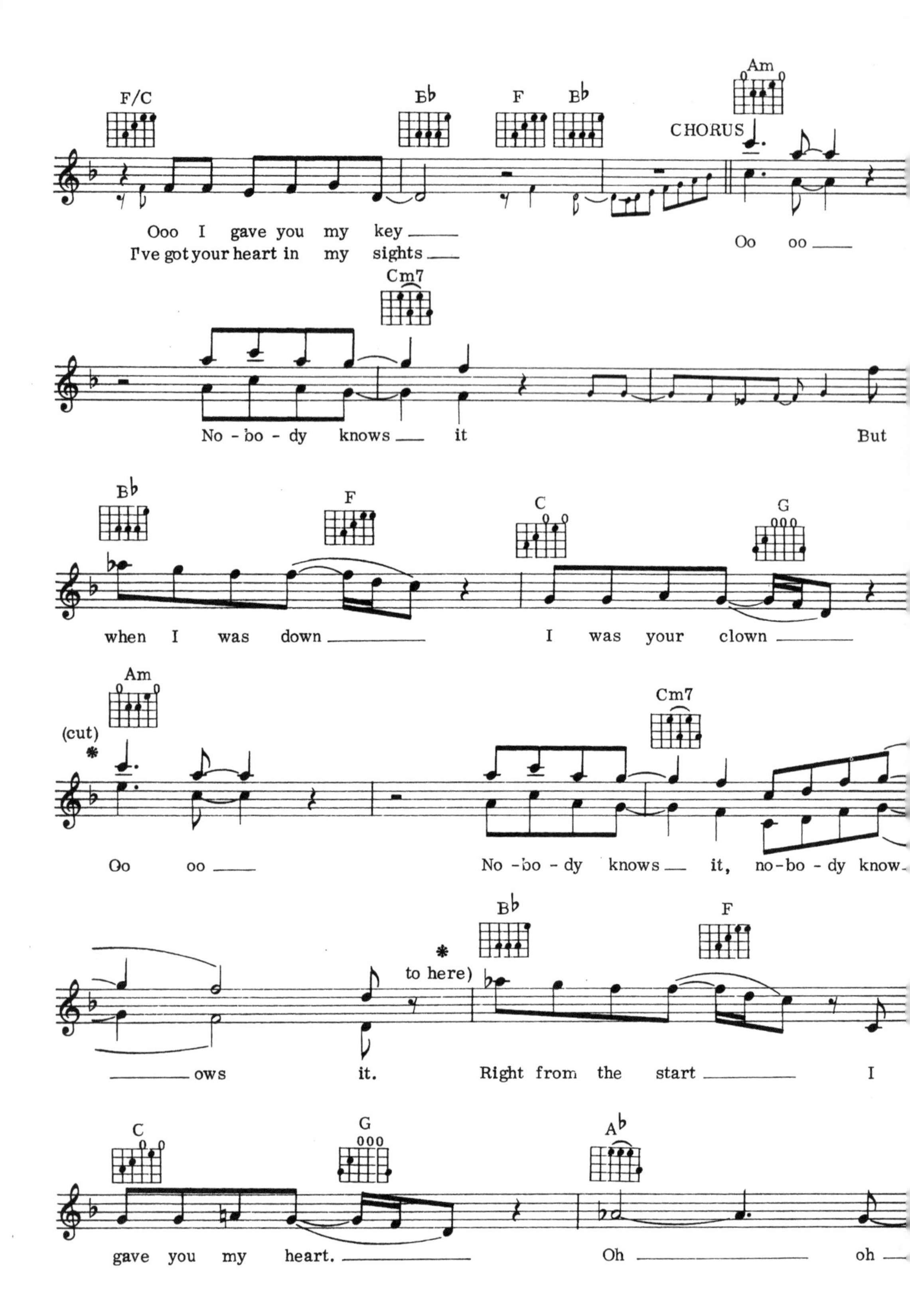
F/C
Bb
F
Bb
Am
CHORUS
Ooo I gave you my key
I've got your heart in my sights
Oo oo
Cm7
No - bo - dy knows it
But
Bb
F
C
G
when I was down
I was your clown
Am
(cut)
*
Oo oo
Cm7
No - bo - dy knows it, no - bo - dy know-
ows it.
*
to here)
Bb
F
Right from the start
I
C
G
Ab
gave you my heart.
Oh
oh

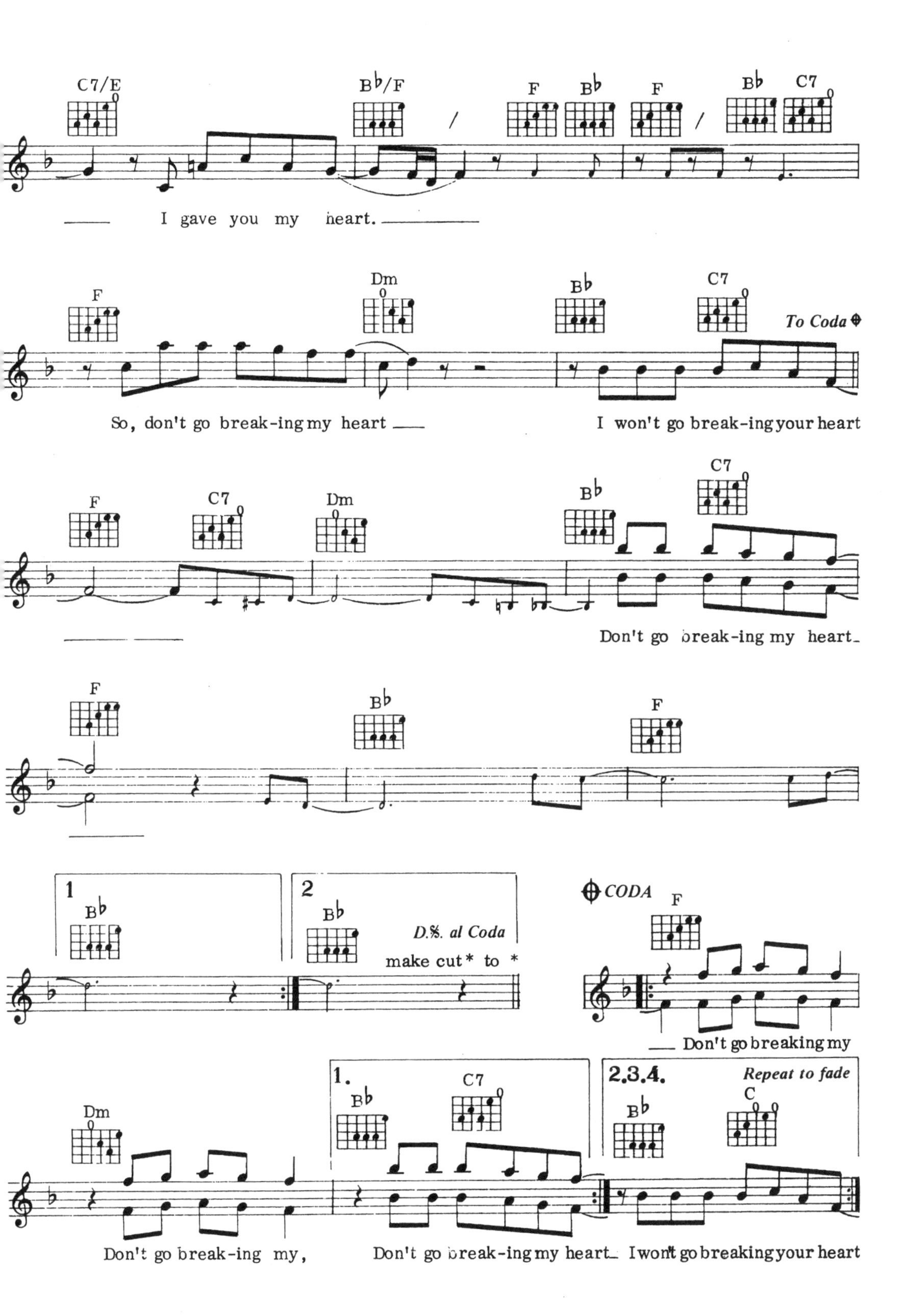
C7/E
B♭/F
F
B♭
F
B♭
C7
I gave you my heart.
F
Dm
B♭
C7
To Coda
So, don't go break-ing my heart
I won't go break-ing your heart
F
C7
Dm
B♭
C7
Don't go break-ing my heart
F
B♭
F
1
B♭
2
B♭
D.%. al Coda
make cut * to *
CODA
F
Don't go breaking my
Dm
1.
B♭
C7
2.3.4.
Repeat to fade
B♭
C
Don't go break-ing my,
Don't go break-ing my heart
I won't go breaking your heart

10

EVERY BREATH YOU TAKE

Words & Music by Sting

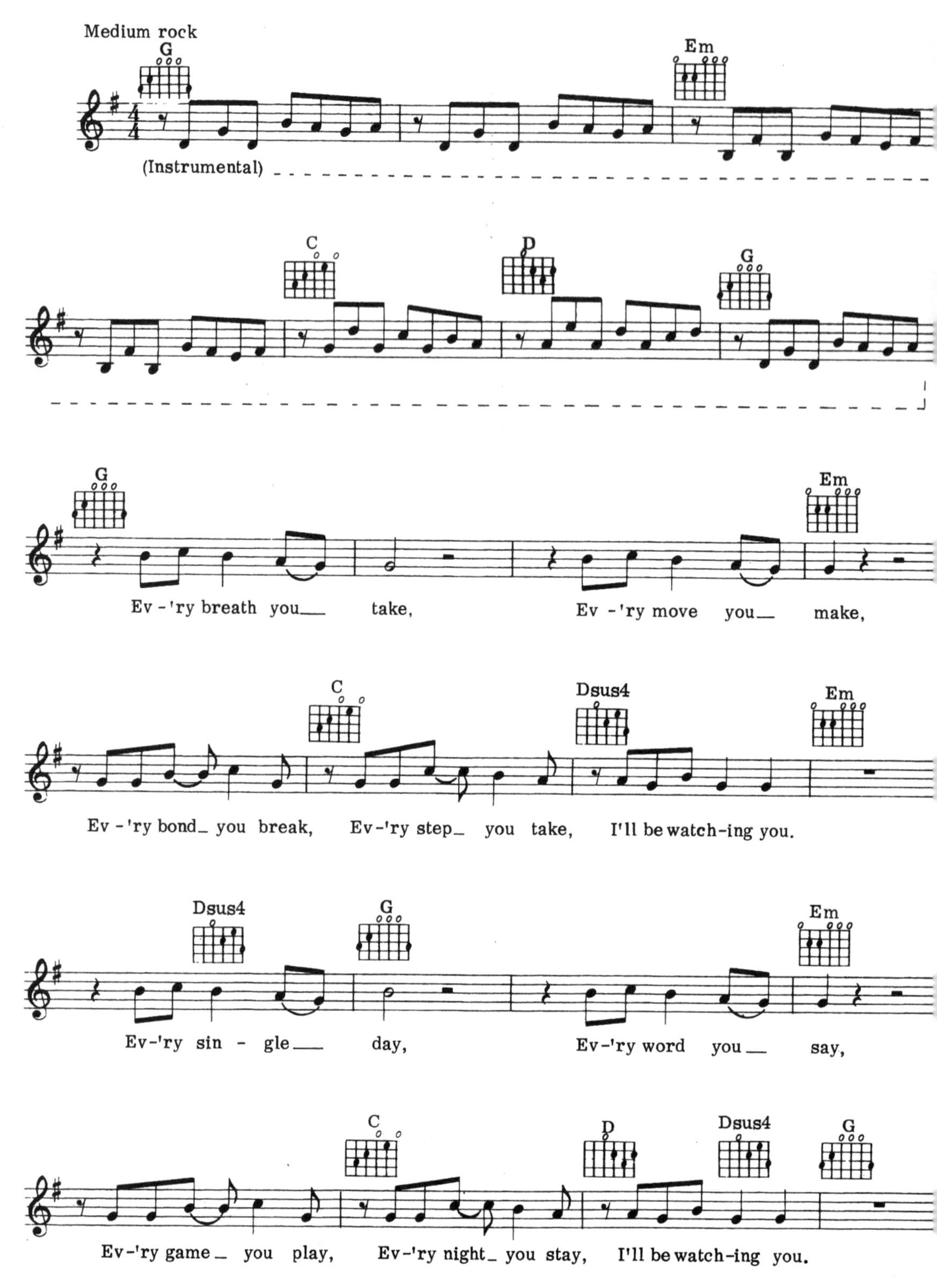
Medium rock
G
Em
(Instrumental)
C
D
G
G
Em
Ev - 'ry breath you take,
Ev - 'ry move you make,
C
Dsus4
Em
Ev - 'ry bond you break, Ev - 'ry step you take, I'll be watch - ing you.
Dsus4
G
Em
Ev - 'ry sin - gle day, Ev - 'ry word you say,
C
D
Dsus4
G
Ev - 'ry game you play, Ev - 'ry night you stay, I'll be watch - ing you.

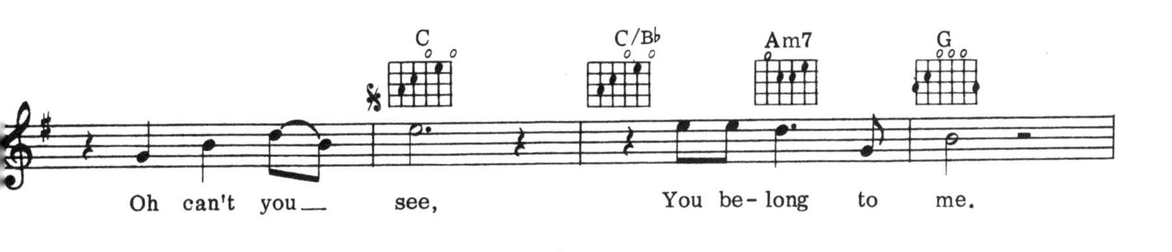
C
C/B♭
Am7
G
Oh can't you see, You be-long to me.

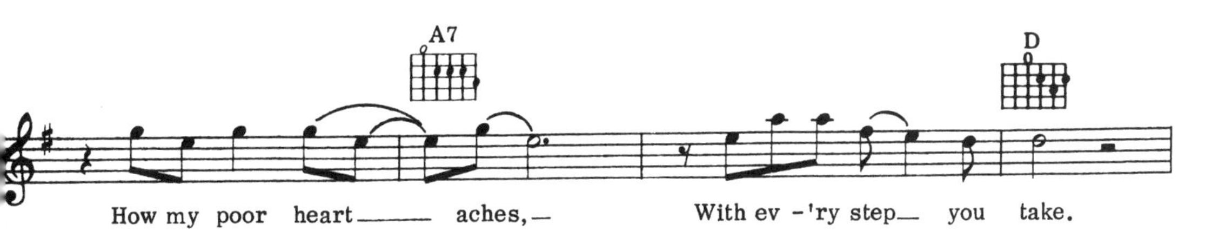
A7
D
How my poor heart aches, With ev-'ry step you take.

Dsus4
G
Em
Ev-'ry move you make, Ev-'ry vow you break,

C
D
Dsus4
Ev-'ry smile you take, Ev-'ry claim you stake, I'll be watch-ing you.

Em
al Coda
E♭
(Instrumental)
Since you've gone, I been lost

F
with-out a trace; I dream at night I can on - ly see your face.

E♭
F
I look a - round but it's you I can't__ re-place; I feel so cold and I
E♭
long for your__ em-brace. I keep cry - ing bab - y, bab - y please.__
G
Em
(Instrumental)
C
D
Em
G
D. S. al Coda
Oh can't you
CODA
Em
C
D
Dsus4
Em
Ev-'ry move_you make, Ev-'ry step_ you take, I'll be watch-ing you. (Instr.)
Dsus4
G
I'll be watch-ing you.

Every Loser Wins

Words & Music by Simon May, Stewart James & Bradley James

Gently
Bb7
Eb
Bb
We near - ly made it we near - ly found the per-
made it could we be sure that it
Ab
Eb
Bb
fect com - bi - na - tion the road was right we
was for the bet - ter who could say we
Ab
Eb
Am7-5
Abmaj7
must have read the signs wrong and now it's all gone.
would have stayed to - geth - er no-thing is cer - tain.
1
Eb
Fm7
Bb7
But if we'd
2
Eb
In a
Fm7
Bb7
Eb
Ab
chang - ing world Eve - ry lo - ser wins

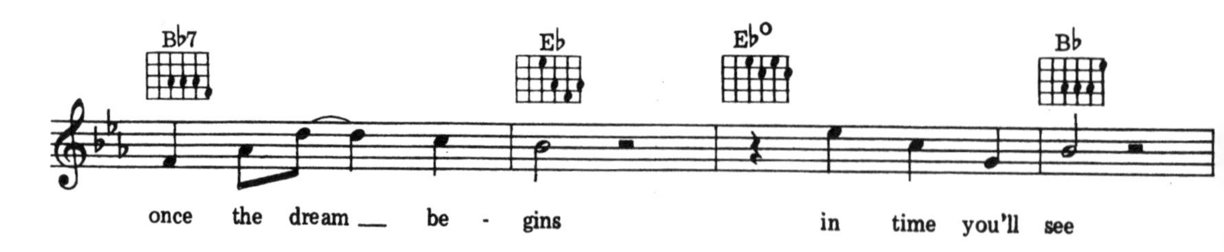
Bb7
Eb
Ebo
Bb
once the dream — be - gins
in time you'll see
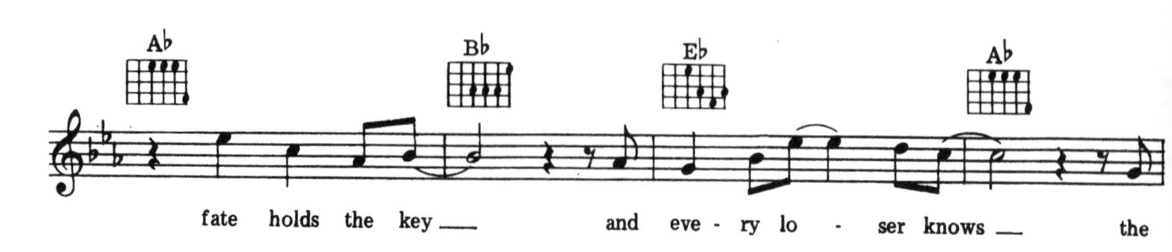
Ab
Bb
Eb
Ab
fate holds the key —
and eve - ry lo - ser knows — the
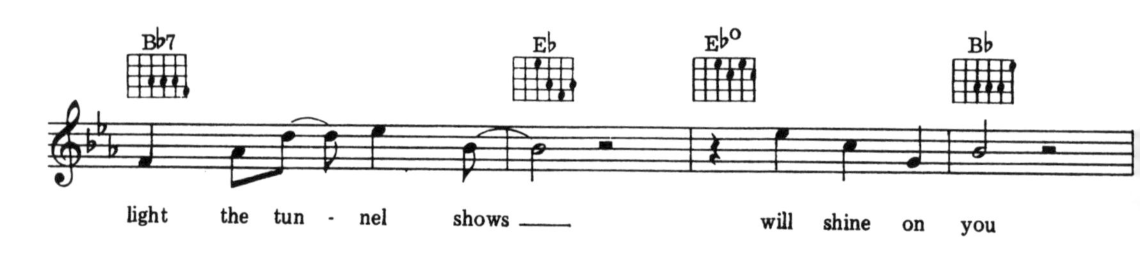
Bb7
Eb
Ebo
Bb
light the tun - nel shows —
will shine on you
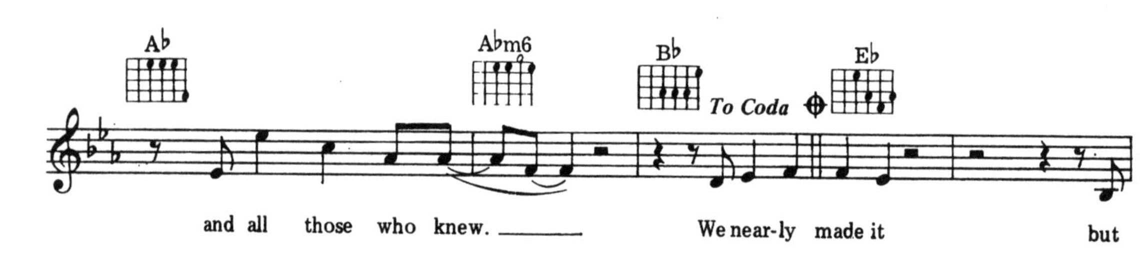
Ab
Abm6
Bb
To Coda
Eb
and all those who knew. —
We near-ly made it
but

Bb
Ab
Eb
sud - den-ly — we seem — to stop and — lose our way

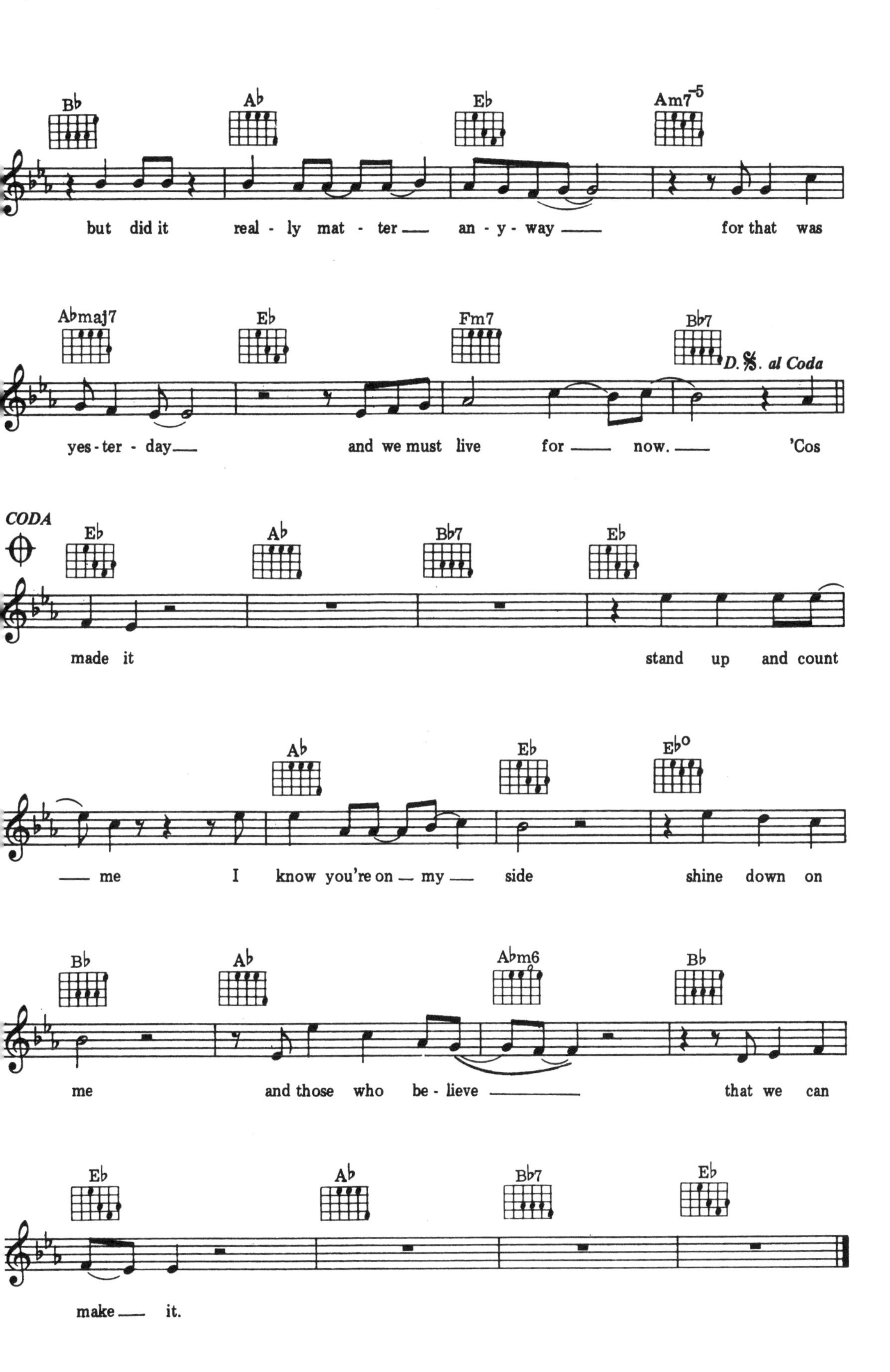

B♭
A♭
E♭
Am7-5
but did it real - ly mat - ter anyway
for that was
A♭maj7
E♭
Fm7
B♭7
D.S. al Coda
yes-ter-day
and we must live for now.
'Cos
CODA
E♭
A♭
B♭7
E♭
made it
stand up and count
A♭
E♭
E♭°
me
I know you're on my side
shine down on
B♭
A♭
A♭m6
B♭
me
and those who be - lieve
that we can
E♭
A♭
B♭7
E♭
make it.

12

Every Little Thing She Does Is Magic

Words & Music by Sting

G G/A G/B A/C♯ G G/A
last
Though I've tried be-fore_ to tell_her of the feel
have to tell_the stor-y of a tho
G/B A/C♯ G G/A G/B A/C♯
3
ings I have for her in_ my_ heart_ ev-'ry tim
sand rain-y days_ since we first_ met._ It's a big
G G/A G/B A/C♯ D
_ that I_ come near_her I_ just lose_ my nerve_ as I've_done from the start
_ en-ough_ um-brel-la but_ it's al-ways me_that ends_up get-ting wet..
G A D G A D G A D A
Ev-'ry lit-tle
A D A D
thing she does_ is mag-ic, ev-'ry-thing she do just turns_ me on,_ ev-en though my

A D A Bb C/F
life be-fore_was trag-ic, now I know my love for her_goes on.
1 G G/A G/B A/C#
2 Bb C/F Bb C/F
Do I
Bb Am7 Gm7 Am7 Gm7 Am7
I re-solved to call_her up a thou-sand times a day, and ask her if she'll mar-ry me
Bb Am7 Bb C
in some old_ fash-ioned way._ But my si-lent fears have gripped me long be-fore.
Bb C Bb C
_ I reach_the phone,_ long be-fore_ my time_has tripped me, must I
Bb C D G A D A A D
al-ways be a-lone. Ev-'ry lit-tle thing she does_is mag-ic, ev-'ry-thing she
to FADE
A D A D D
do just turns me on,_ev-en though my life before_was trag-ic now I know my love for her_goes on._Ev-'ry lit-tle

13
FERNANDO

Words & Music by Benny Andersson, Björn Ulvaeus & Stig Anderson

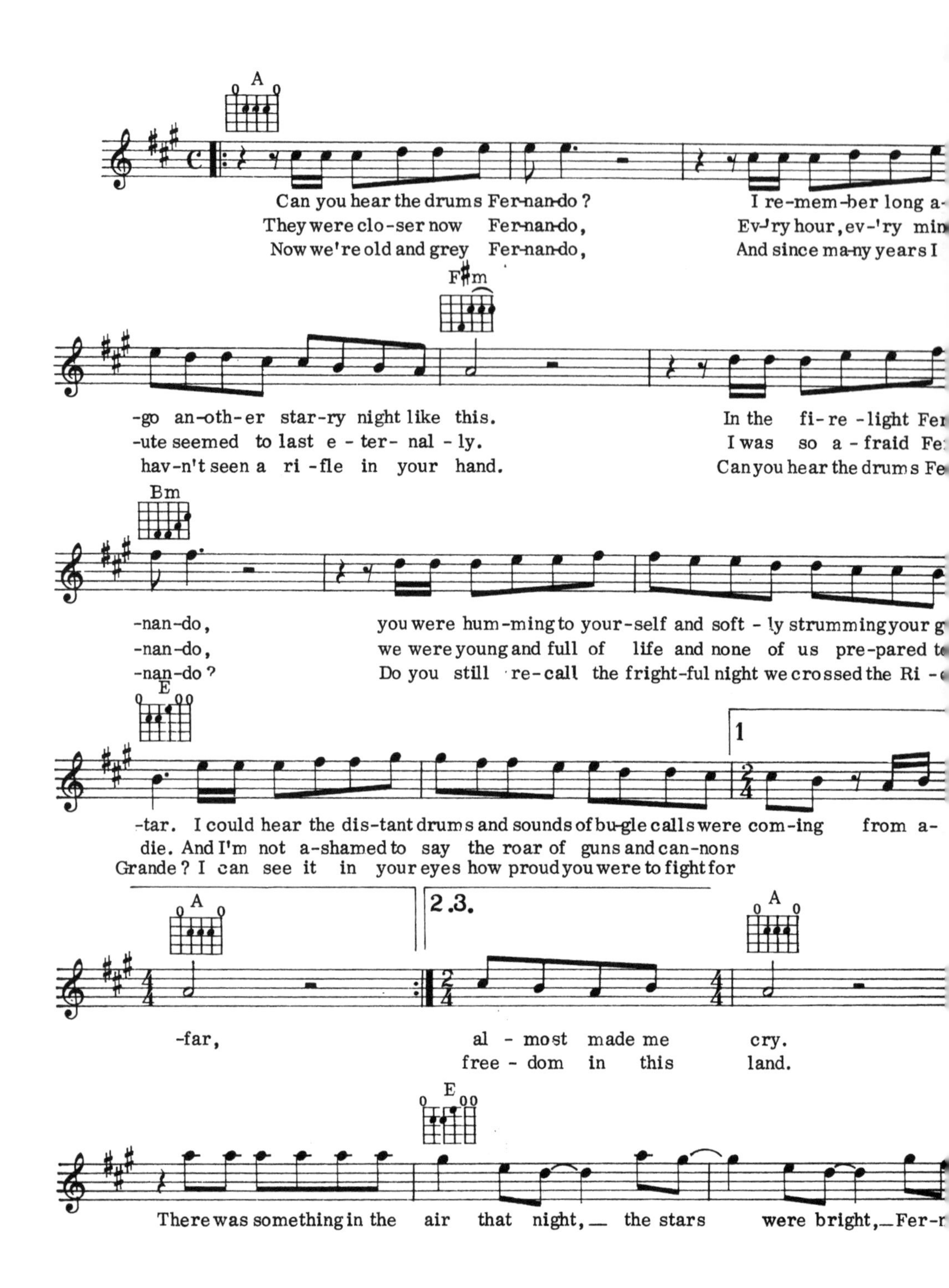

A
Can you hear the drums Fer-nan-do? I re-mem-ber long a-
They were clo-ser now Fer-nan-do, Ev-'ry hour, ev-'ry min
Now we're old and grey Fer-nan-do, And since ma-ny years I
F#m
-go an-oth-er star-ry night like this. In the fi-re-light Fer
-ute seemed to last e-ter-nal-ly. I was so a-fraid Fe
hav-n't seen a ri-fle in your hand. Can you hear the drums Fe
Bm
-nan-do, you were hum-ming to your-self and soft-ly strumming your g
-nan-do, we were young and full of life and none of us pre-pared t
-nan-do? Do you still re-call the fright-ful night we crossed the Ri-
E
1
-tar. I could hear the dis-tant drums and sounds of bu-gle calls were com-ing from a-
die. And I'm not a-shamed to say the roar of guns and can-nons
Grande? I can see it in your eyes how proud you were to fight for
A
2.3.
A
-far, al-most made me cry.
free-dom in this land.
E
There was something in the air that night, the stars were bright, Fer-

A
E
- do. They were shin-ing there for you and me, — for li -
A
G°
- ber - ty, Fer- nan - do. Though we nev-er thought that we could lose —
F♯
B7
B7
— there's no re - gret. — If I had to do the
E
1 A
same a - gain, — I would — my friend, — Fer-nan - do
2 D
To Coda
A
- do.
E
D.C. al Coda
3
CODA
B7
E
If I had to do the same a - gain, — I would —
A
Repeat to fade
— my friend — Fer-nan - do. If I had to do the

14

Get Back

Words & Music by John Lennon & Paul McCartney

Very brightly

F
F7
B♭
Jo - jo was a man who thought he was a lo-ner, but he knew it could-n't last.
Sweet Lo-ret-ta Mar-tin thought she was a wo-man, but she was an-oth-er man.

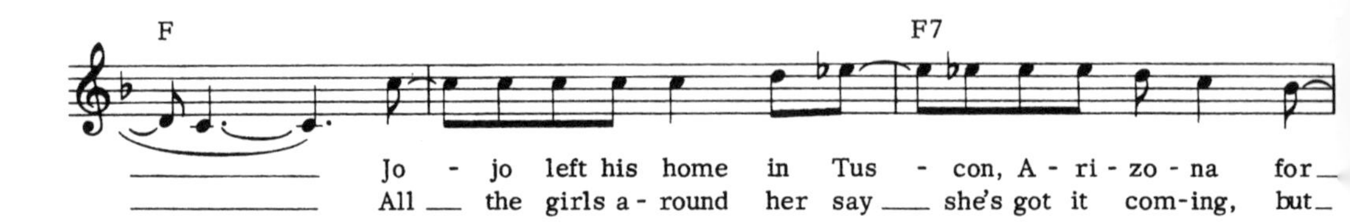

F
F7
Jo - jo left his home in Tus - con, A - ri - zo - na for
All the girls a - round her say she's got it com-ing, but

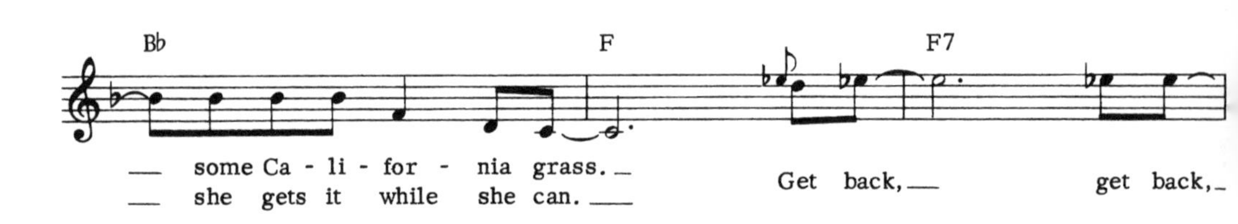

B♭
F
F7
some Ca - li - for - nia grass.
she gets it while she can.
Get back, get back,

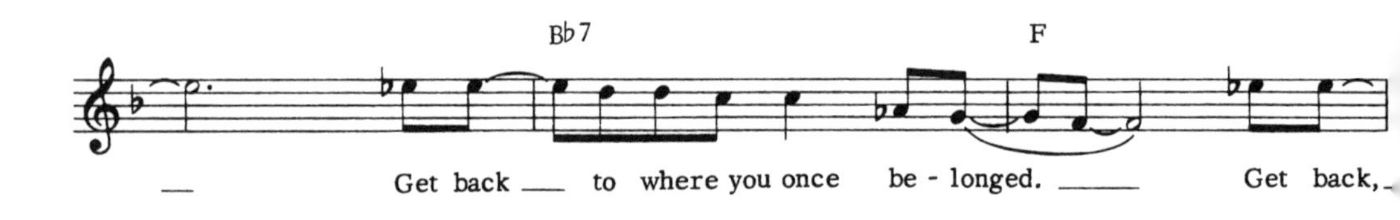

B♭7
F
Get back to where you once be - longed. Get back,

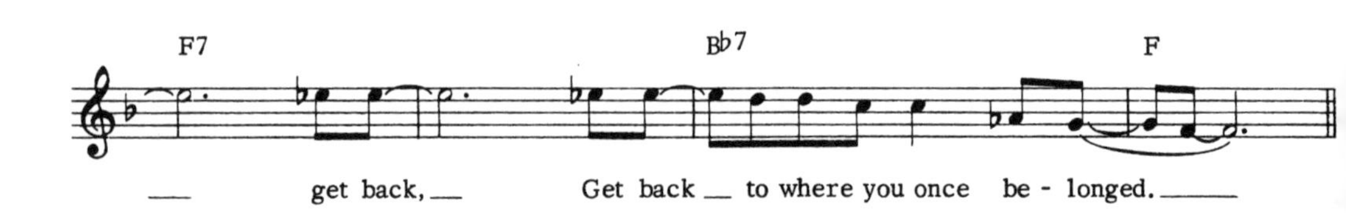

F7
B♭7
F
get back, Get back to where you once be - longed.

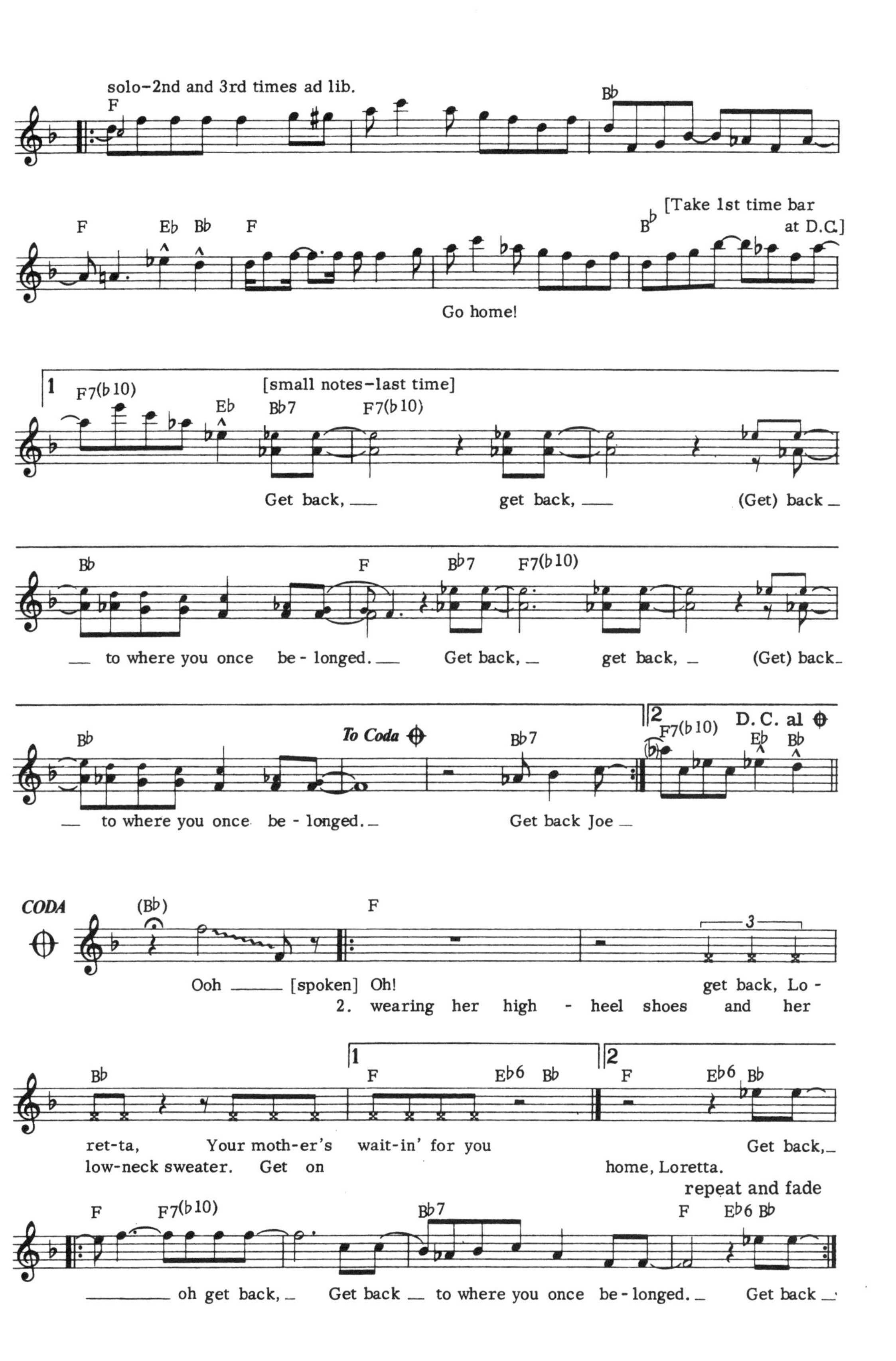
solo–2nd and 3rd times ad lib.
F
Bb
F
Eb
Bb
F
Bb
[Take 1st time bar at D.C.]
Go home!
1
F7(b10)
Eb
[small notes–last time]
Bb7
F7(b10)
Get back,
get back,
(Get) back
Bb
F
Bb7
F7(b10)
to where you once be-longed.
Get back,
get back,
(Get) back
Bb
To Coda
Bb7
2
F7(b10)
D. C. al
Eb
Bb
to where you once be-longed.
Get back Joe
CODA
(Bb)
F
3
Ooh
[spoken] Oh!
get back, Lo-
2. wearing her high-heel shoes and her
Bb
1
F
Eb6
Bb
2
F
Eb6
Bb
ret-ta, Your moth-er's wait-in' for you
Get back,
low-neck sweater. Get on home, Loretta.
repeat and fade
F
F7(b10)
Bb7
F
Eb6
Bb
oh get back,
Get back
to where you once be-longed.
Get back

15
GET IT ON

Words & Music by Marc Bolan

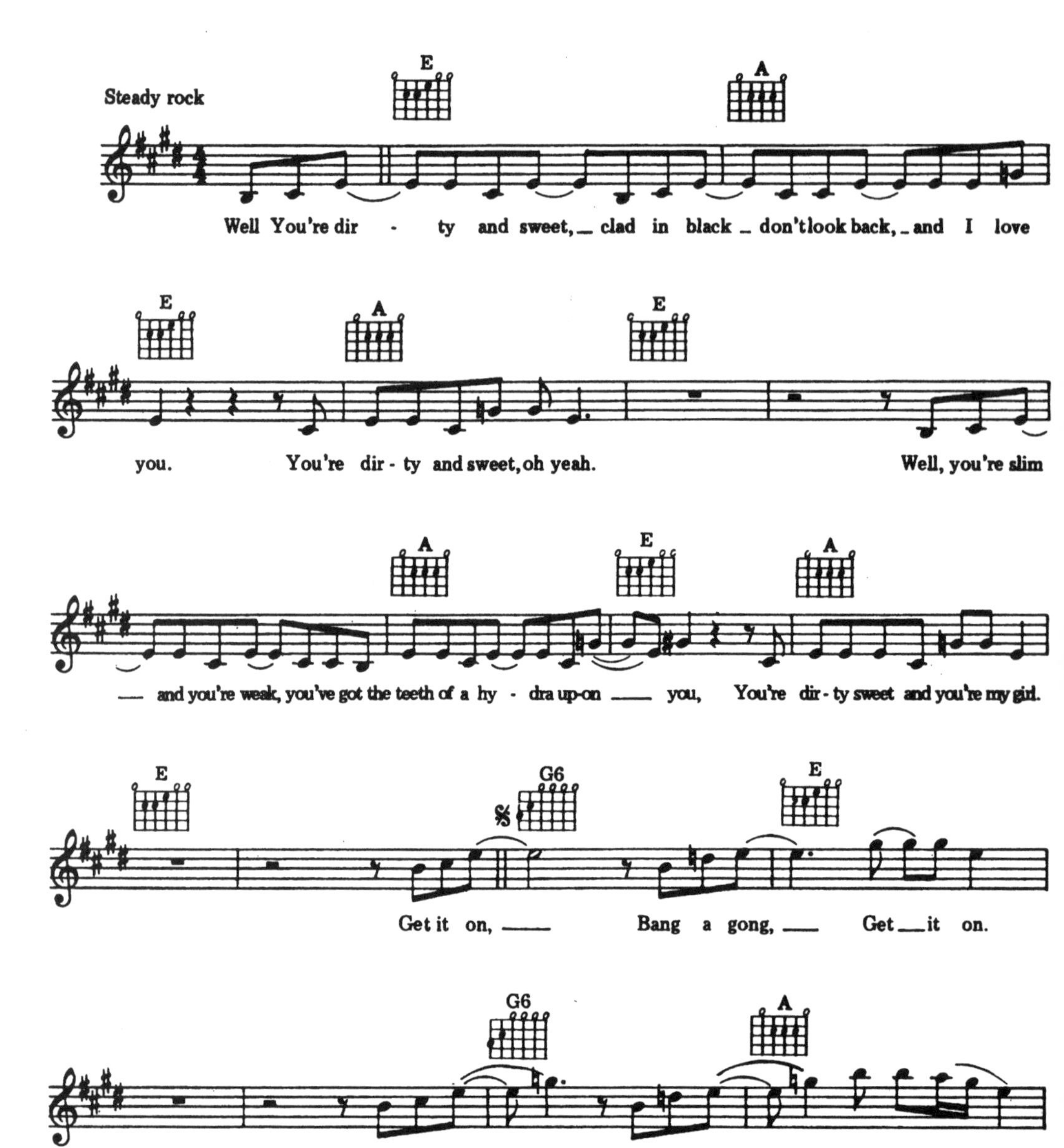
Steady rock
E
A
Well You're dir - ty and sweet, clad in black don't look back, and I love
you. You're dir - ty and sweet, oh yeah. Well, you're slim
and you're weak, you've got the teeth of a hy - dra up-on you, You're dir - ty sweet and you're my girl.
G6
Get it on, Bang a gong, Get it on.
Get it on, Bang a gong, Get it on.

To Coda
E
Well, you're built like a car you've got a

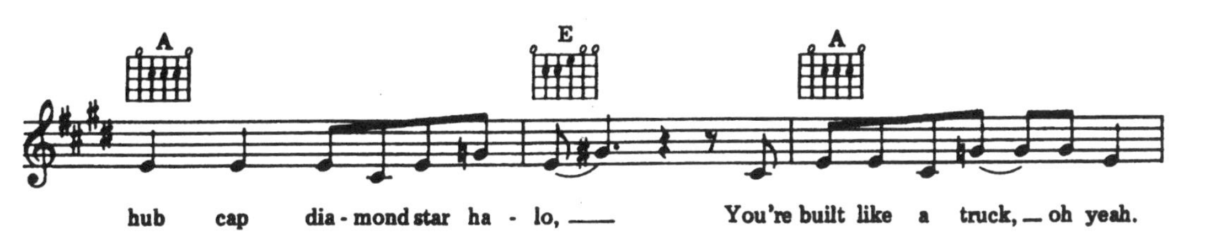
A
E
A
hub cap dia - mond star ha - lo,
You're built like a truck, oh yeah.

E
You're an un - tanned youth, thats the truth

A
E
A
with your cloak full of ea - gles,
You're dir - ty sweet and you're my girl.

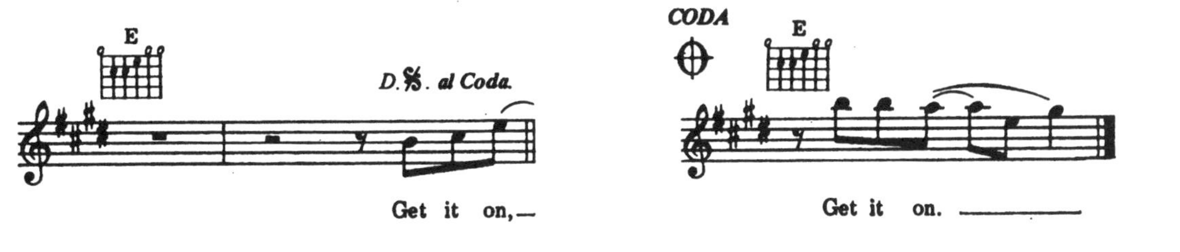
E
D.%. al Coda
Get it on,
CODA
E
Get it on.

16

GLAD ALL OVER

Words & Music by Dave Clark & Mike Smith

Moderato
C F C F C F
You say that you love me all of the time,
hap - py you'll ne-ver be blue,
C F C F C F C F
You say that you need me, you'll al-ways be mine.
You'll have no sor- row, for I'll al-ways be true.
C G7 C
tacet
I'm feel - in' glad all o - ver, glad all o-
And I'm feel - in' glad all o - ver, glad all o-
A♭9 G7 C F
- ver, Ba -by I'm glad all o - ver, so glad you're mine.
- ver, Ba- by I'm glad all o - ver, so glad you're mine.
1 C F 2 C F A♭
I'll make you Oth-er girls may try to take me a-

C
F
C
F
-way.
But you know
G
G7+
3
here by your side I will stay, I - I - I'll stay. Our love will
C
F
C
F
C
F
last now till the end of time.
C
F
C
F
C
F
Be - cause this love now is on - ly yours and
C
F
C
G7
mine. And I'm feel - in' glad all o-
C
A♭9
- ver, glad all o - ver, Ba - by I'm
G7
C
F
C
glad all o - er, so glad you're mine.

A Good Heart

Words & Music by Maria McKee

Moderato
Bb
Gm7
F
Bb
I've heard a lot of sto - ries, I sup - pose they could be true,
Eb
Bb
F
Bb
Gm7
all a - bout love and what it can do to you. High is the risk of stri-king out, the
F
Bb
F
Eb
risk of get - ting hurt, and still I have so much to learn. Well I know
Bb
'cause I think a - bout it all the time. I know
Eb
F
that real love is quite a prize. And a
Bb
F
Gm
Eb
Bb
Eb
good heart these days is hard to find, true love, the

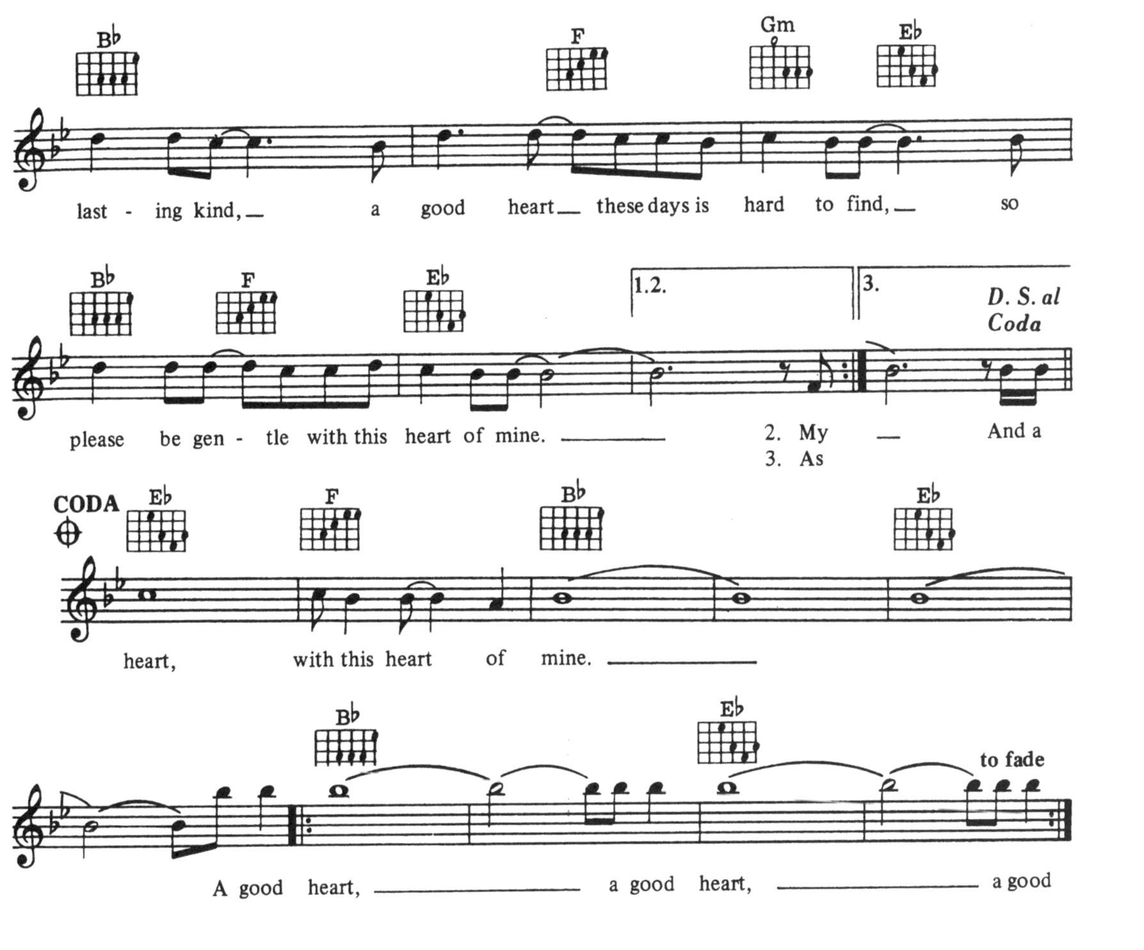
Bb
F
Gm
Eb
last - ing kind, a good heart these days is hard to find, so
Bb
F
Eb
1.2.
3.
D. S. al Coda
please be gen - tle with this heart of mine.
2. My
3. As
And a
CODA
Eb
F
Bb
Eb
heart, with this heart of mine.
Bb
Eb
to fade
A good heart, a good heart, a good

2. My expectations may be high, I blame that on my youth,
Soon enough I'll learn the fateful truth.
I'll face it like a fighter, then boast of how I've grown,
Anything is better than being alone.
Well I know 'cause I learn a little every day,
I know 'cause I listen when the experts say: that a good love . . . .

3. As I reflect on all my childhood dreams,
My ideas of love weren't as foolish as they seemed.
If I don't start looking now then I'll be left behind
And a good heart these days is hard to find.
I know it's a dream I'm willing to defend,
I know it will be worth it in the end.

18
GOODNIGHT GIRL

Words & Music by Graeme Clark, Tom Cunningham, Neil Mitchell & Marti Pellow

♩ = 90
A
Dmaj7
You hear me so clear - ly and see how I
keep me so near you and see me so
A
Dmaj7
try; you feel me so heal me and tear me a -
far; and hold me and send me deep in your
Gmaj7
A
part. And I won't tell a soul, I won't tell at all
heart. And I won't tell a soul, I won't tell at all
Gmaj7
Bm7
and do they have to know
and I won't let them know
a -
Bm7/E
A
bout my good - night girl.
Caught up in your wish - ing well, your hopes in - side it,
F♯m7
1.
Bm7
take your love and pro - mis - es and make them last, you

Bm7/E
2.
Bm7
Bm7/E
make them last.
2. You
You make them last.
A
Caught up in your wish - ing well, your hopes in - side it,
F#m7
Bm7
take your love and pro - mis - es and make them last, you
Bm7/E
Fine
Dmaj9
Amaj7
make them last.
Does - n't mat - ter how sad I made you,
Dmaj9
Amaj7
does - n't mat - ter how hard I've tried.
Dmaj9
Amaj7
Just re - mem - ber the same old rea - son re -
Cmaj7
D.S. al Fine
flec - ted in your eyes, you said you wan - ted me.

19

(Everything I Do) I Do It For You

Words by Bryan Adams & Robert John 'Mutt' Lange
Music by Michael Kamen

Moderately
C
G/C
1. Look in - to my eyes you will see
(See lyric 2)
F/C
Cadd9
C
what you mean to me. Search your heart, search your
G/C
F/C
soul, and when you find me there you'll
C/G
G
Dm
C
search no more. Don't tell me it's not worth try - in'
Dm
C
for, you can't tell me it's not worth dy - in'
Dm
C
for. You know it's true ev - ery - thing I

G
C
1.
2.
do, I do it for you. There's
B♭
E♭
3fr.
B♭
no love like your love and no oth - er could give
F
C
more love, there's no - where un - less
G
D
G
you're there all the time, all the way yeah.
F
C
(Instrumental)
1.
2.
Dm
Oh you can't tell me it's not worth try - in'

G
Dm
for, I can't help it, there's no - thin' I want
G
C
more. Yeah I would fight for you, I'd
G
F
lie for you, walk the wire for you, yeah I'd
Fm
a tempo
C/G
die for you. You know it's true, ev - ery - thing I
G
rall.
F
Dm
C
do, oh, I do it for you.

2. Look into your heart
You will find there's nothin' there to hide
Take me as I am, take my life
I would give it all, I would sacrifice.

Don't tell me it's not worth fightin' for
I can't help it, there's nothin' I want more
You know it's true, everything I do
I do it for you.

20

A Hard Day's Night

Words & Music by John Lennon & Paul McCartney

Moderato
C F C
1.3. It's been a Hard Day's Night, And I've been
work all day To get you
B♭6 C F
work-ing like a dog. It's been a Hard Day's Night
mon-ey to buy you things, And it's worth it just to hear you say
C B♭6 C
I should be sleep-ing like a log. But when I
You're gon-na give me ev-'ry-thing. So why I
F G7
get home to you, I find the thing that you do Will make me
love to come home, 'Cos when I get you a-lone You know I'll
To Coda
C F7 C C Em
feel al-right. 2. You know I
be o-kay. When I'm home
Am Em C
ev-'ry-thing seems to be al-right. When I'm home
Am F6 G7
D.S. al Coda
feel-ing you hold-ing me tight, tight. Yeah, 3. It's been a
CODA
C F C F7 C F
right. You know I feel al-right You know I
C F7 B♭6 C
feel al-right.

HELP!

Words & Music by John Lennon & Paul McCartney

Moderately
Am
Am7
F
3
Help! I need some - bod - y, Help! Not just
D7
G
an - y - bod - y. Help! You know I need some-one, Help!
G
Bm
1.3. When I was young - er, so much young-er than to-
2. And now my life has changed, in, oh, so man - y
Em
C
F
-day, I nev-er need - ed an - y - bod-y's help in an-y way.
ways, My in - de - pen-dence seems to van - ish in the haze.
G
But now these days are gone, I'm
But ev - 'ry now and then I

Bm
Em
not so self as - sured.
feel so in - se - cure,
Now I find I've changed my mind, I've
I know that I just need you like I've
C
F
G
Am
o - pened up the doors.
nev - er done be - fore.
Help me if you can, I'm feel - ing
F
down,
And I do ap - pre - ci - ate you be-ing 'round
D7
Help me get my feet back on the ground
G
1
Won't you please, please help me?
2
please help me?
Em
G
Help me! Help me! Oo.

HOUSE OF THE RISING SUN

Traditional, arranged by Alan Price

VERSE 1
Slow Beat
Dm F G B♭ Dm F
1. There is a house in New Or-leans, They call the Ris - ing
A7 Dm F G B♭ Dm A7
Sun. And it's been the ruin of man-y a poor boy, And God, I know I'm
Dm F G B♭ Dm A7
one.
Dm A7
VERSES 2 & 3
Dm F G B♭
2. My moth - er was a tai - lor,
on - ly thing a gamb-ler needs Is a
Dm F A7 Dm F G B♭
Sewed my new blue jeans, My fath - er was a gam - blin' man
suit - case and a trunk, And the on - ly time he'll be sat-is-fied Is
Dm A7 Dm F G B♭
Down in New - Or-leans.
when he's all a - drunk.
Dm A7
1 Dm A7
2 Dm A7
3. Now the
4. Oh!

VERSE 4
Dm F G B♭ Dm F A7
moth-er, tell your child-ren, Not to do what I have done.
Dm F G B♭ Dm A7
Spend your lives in sin and mis-er-y In the house of the Ris - ing
Dm F G B♭
Sun.
Dm A7 Dm A7
VERSES 5 & 6
Dm F
5. Well I've got one foot on the
is a house in
G B♭ Dm F A7
plat - form The oth - er foot on the train, I'm
New Or - leans They call the Ris - ing Sun. And it's
Dm F G B♭ Dm A7
go - ing back to New Or - leans To wear that ball and
been the ruin of man-y a poor boy, And God, I know I'm
Dm F G B♭
chain.
one.
Dm A7
1 Dm A7
6. Well, there
2 Dm

How Deep Is Your Love

Words & Music by Barry Gibb, Robin Gibb & Maurice Gibb

Moderato
E♭ 6 fr.
E♭maj7 6 fr.
A♭maj7 4 fr.
A♭/B♭ 4 fr.
I know your
E♭ 6 fr.
Gm7 3 fr.
Fm7
C7 3 fr.
Fm7
G7 3 fr.
eyes in the morn - ing sun. I feel you touch me in the pour - ing rain.
I be - lieve in you. You know the door to my ver - y soul.
A♭/B♭ 4 fr.
E♭ 6 fr.
Gm7 3 fr.
Cm7 3 fr.
And the mo - ment that you wan-der far from me, I wan - na
You're the light in my deep-est, dark - est hour; you're my
Fm7
A♭/B♭ 4 fr.
A♭maj7 4 fr.
feel you in my arms a - gain. And you come to me on a sum -
sav - ior when I fall. And you may not think I care
Gm7 3 fr.
Fm7
mer breeze; keep me warm in your love, then you soft -
for you when you know down in - side that I real -

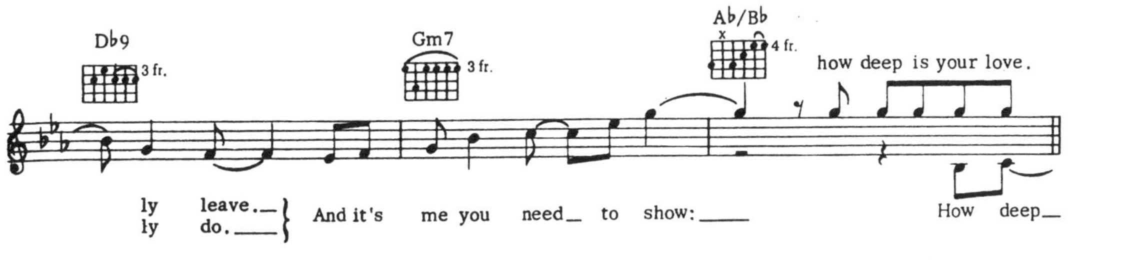
Db9
3 fr.
Gm7
3 fr.
Ab/Bb
4 fr.
how deep is your love.
ly leave.
ly do.
And it's me you need to show:
How deep

Eb
6 fr.
Ebmaj7
6 fr.
Abmaj7
4 fr.
is your love? How deep is your love? I real-ly mean to learn.

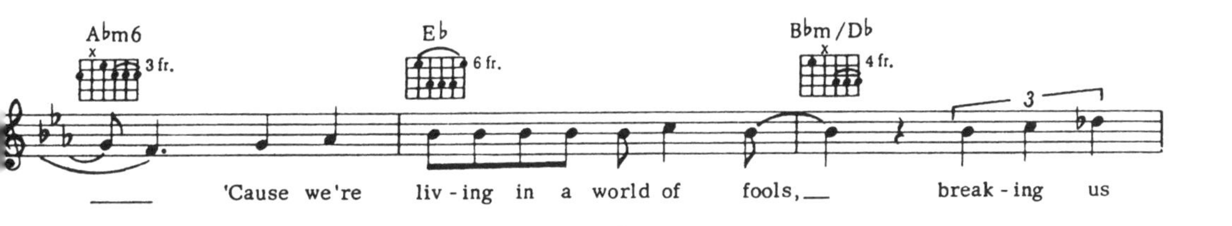
Abm6
3 fr.
Eb
6 fr.
Bbm/Db
4 fr.
3
'Cause we're liv-ing in a world of fools, break-ing us

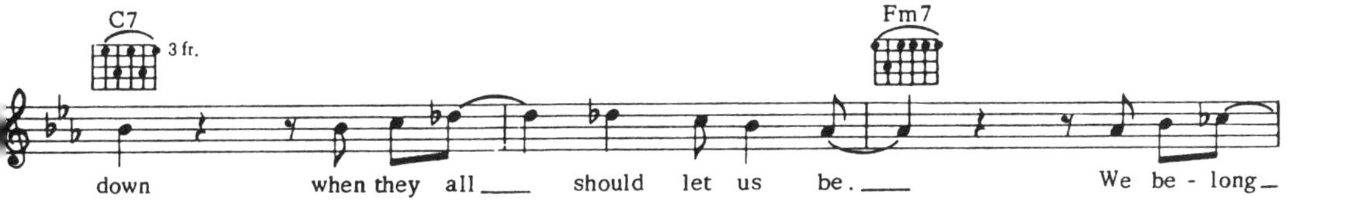
C7
3 fr.
Fm7
down when they all should let us be. We be-long

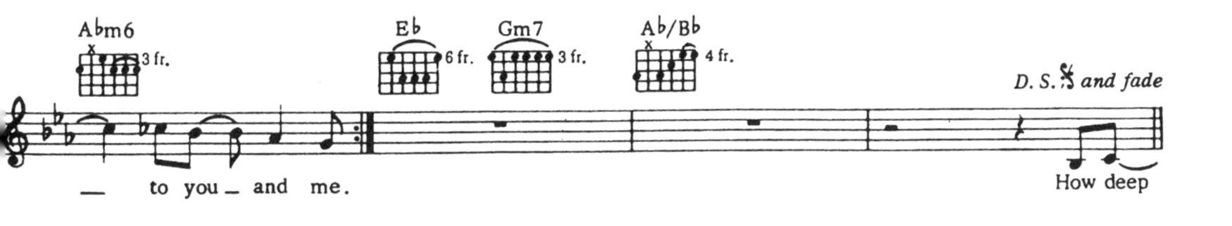
Abm6
3 fr.
Eb
6 fr.
Gm7
3 fr.
Ab/Bb
4 fr.
D. S. and fade
to you and me.
How deep

24
I Can't Stop Loving You

Words & Music by Don Gibson

D
A
So you're leav - ing in the
We took a tax - i to the
Bm
F♯m
morn - ing on the ear - ly train.
sta - tion not a word was said,
G
A6
I could say ev - 'ry-thing's al-
I saw you walk a - cross the
A
G
A6
-right. I could pre - tend and say good-
road, For may - be the last time but I don't
A7
D
A
-bye. Got your tick - et, got your
know. I'm feel- ing hum - ble, I heard a
Bm
F♯m
suit - case, got your leav - ing smile,
rum - ble on the rail - way track,

G
A6
A
I could say that's the way it goes,
And when I hear that whis-tle blow,
G
A6
B♭°
I could pre-tend and you won't know
I walk a-way and you won't know
Bm
A
that I was ly-ing.
D
A
G
'Cause I can't stop lov-ing you, I
D
A
G
can't stop lov-ing you, No I
D
A
G
C
can't stop lov-ing you though I try.
(3) why should I try,
1
G
2
G
D.S. to fade
Why should I try.
I just

25

I Knew You Were Waiting (For Me)

Words & Music by Simon Climie & Dennis Morgan

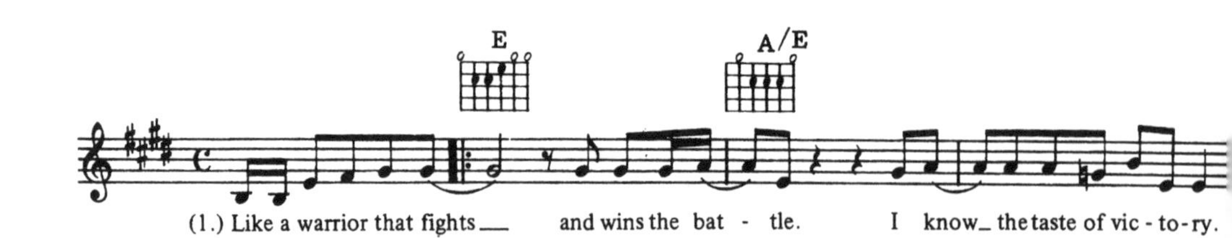
E
A/E
(1.) Like a warrior that fights and wins the bat - tle. I know the taste of vic - to-ry.

E
A/E
Though I went through some nights con-sumed by the sha-dows, I was crip-pled e-mo- tion-ally,

E
F♯m
C♯m7
F♯m7
mm. Somehow I made it through the heart-ache, yes I did, I es-caped

C♯m7
F♯m7
C♯m7
A
I found my way out of the dark-ness, kept my faith, kept my faith.

E
A/E
E
When the ri-ver was deep I did-n't falt - er, when the mountain was high I still be - lieved

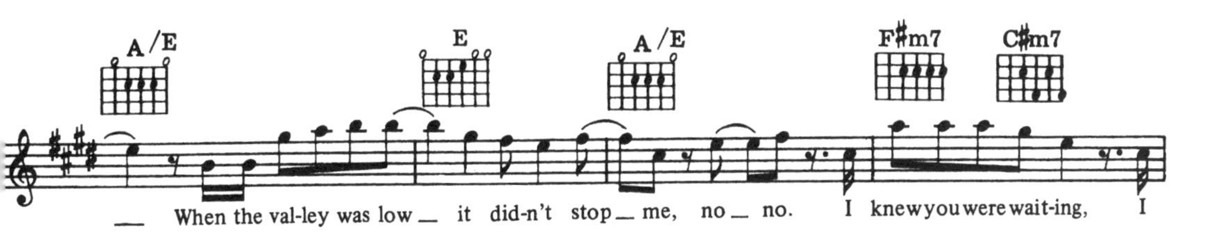
A/E
E
A/E
F#m7
C#m7
When the val-ley was low it did-n't stop me, no no. I knew you were wait-ing, I

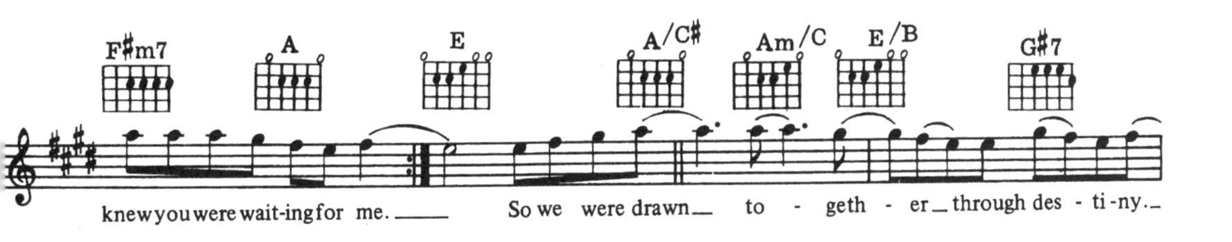
F#m7
A
E
A/C#
Am/C
E/B
G#7
knew you were wait-ing for me. So we were drawn to - geth - er through des - ti - ny.

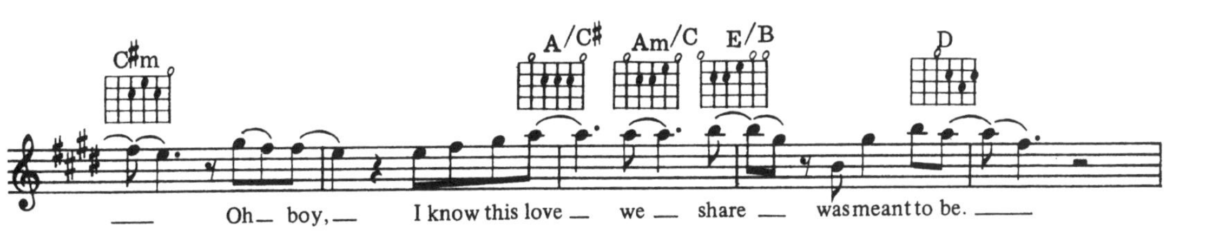
C#m
A/C#
Am/C
E/B
D
Oh boy, I know this love we share was meant to be.

F#m7
C#m7
F#m7
C#m7
F#m7
A
D.S. to FADE
Knew you were wait-ing, knew you were wait-ing, knew you were waiting for me.

VERSE 2:
With an endless desire
I kept on searching
Sure in time our eyes would meet.

And like the bridge is on fire
The hurt is over
One touch and you set me free.

I don't regret a single moment no I don't, looking back
When I think of all those disappointments, I just laugh, I just laugh.

26

I Think We're Alone Now

Words & Music by Ritchie Cordell

Moderately
G
Bm
Em
3
"Child - ren be - have" that's what they say
Look at the way we got - ta hide
D
G
Bm
3
when we're to - geth - er. "And watch how you play."
what we're do - in'. 'Cause what would they say
Em
D
Bm
They don't un - der - stand, And so we're run - ning just as fast as we
if they nev - er knew? And so we're
G
Bm
G
can, Hold - ing on to one an - oth - er's hand,
F
Try - ing to get a - way in - to the night And then you

D7
put your arms a - round me as we tum - ble to the ground And then you

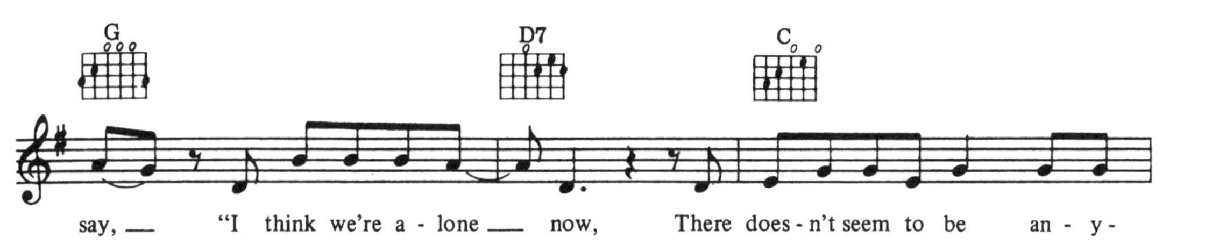
G
D7
C
say, "I think we're a - lone now, There does - n't seem to be an - y -

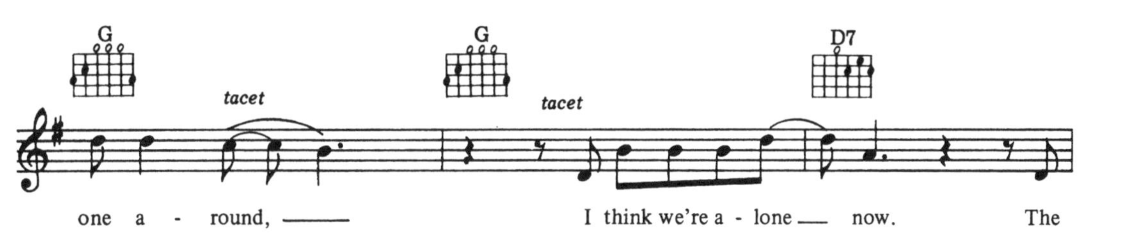
G
G
D7
tacet
tacet
one a - round, I think we're a - lone now. The

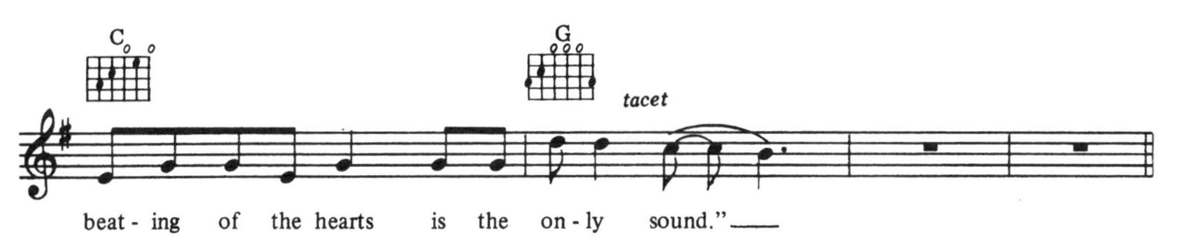
C
G
tacet
beat - ing of the hearts is the on - ly sound."

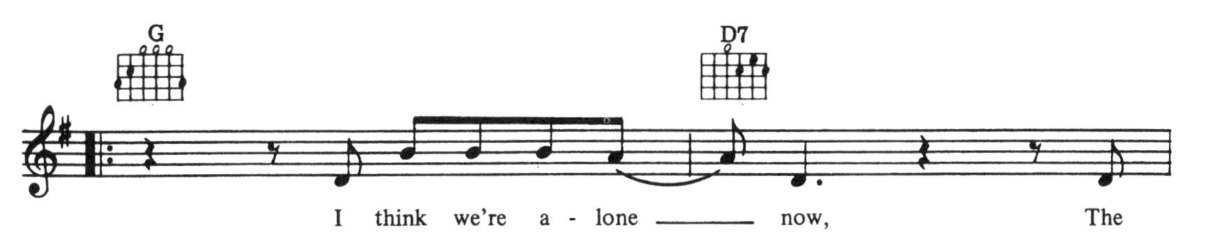
G
D7
I think we're a - lone now, The

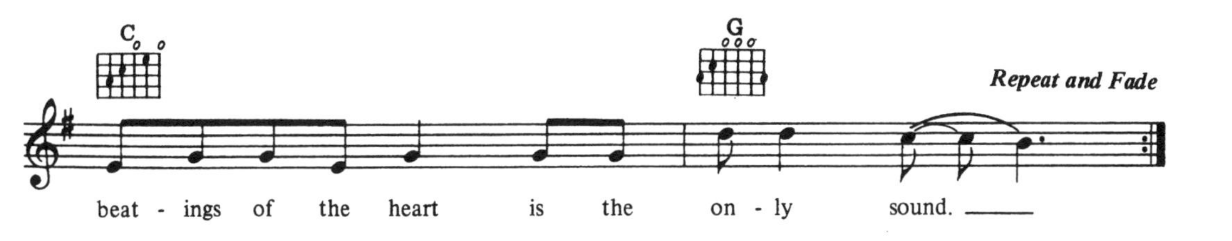
C
G
Repeat and Fade
beat - ings of the heart is the on - ly sound.

27

I Want To Wake Up With You

Words & Music by Ben Peters

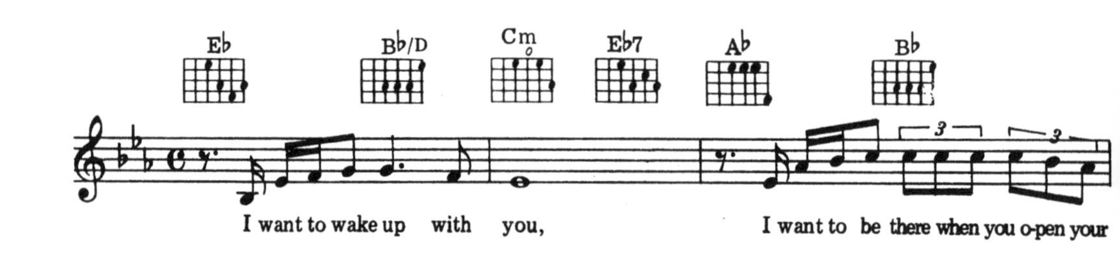

E♭ B♭/D Cm E♭7 A♭ B♭
3 3
I want to wake up with you, I want to be there when you o-pen your

E♭ E♭7 A♭ B♭ Cm A♭ A°
3
eyes, I want you to be the first thing that I see,

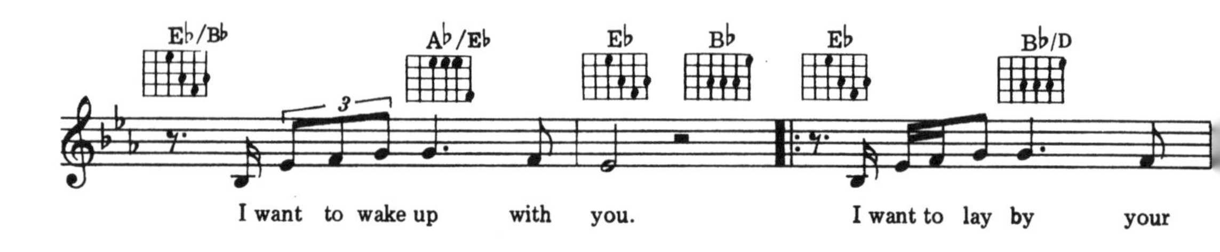

E♭/B♭ A♭/E♭ E♭ B♭ E♭ B♭/D
3
I want to wake up with you. I want to lay by your

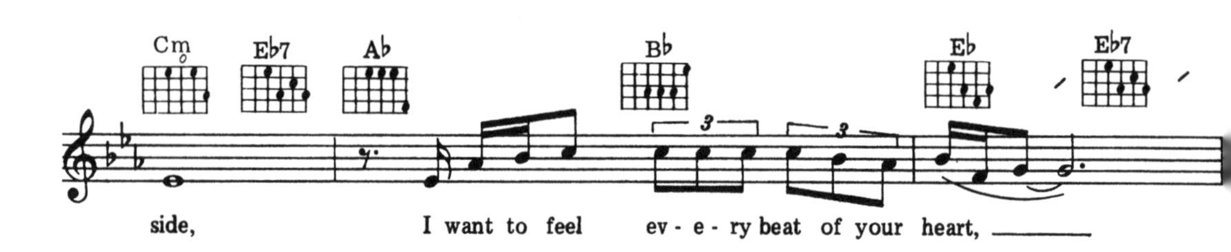

Cm E♭7 A♭ B♭ E♭ E♭7
3 3
side, I want to feel ev - e - ry beat of your heart,

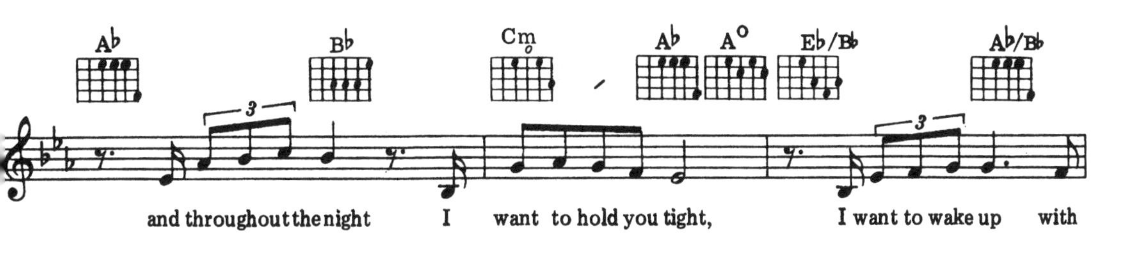
A♭ B♭ Cm A♭ A° E♭/B♭ A♭/B♭
3
and throughout the night I want to hold you tight, I want to wake up with

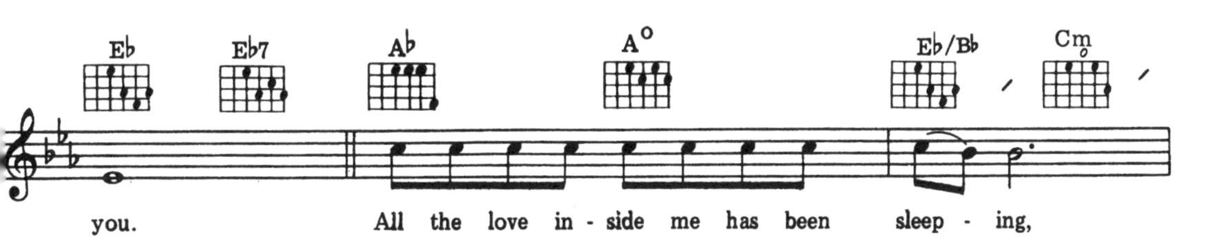
E♭ E♭7 A♭ A° E♭/B♭ Cm
you. All the love in - side me has been sleep - ing,

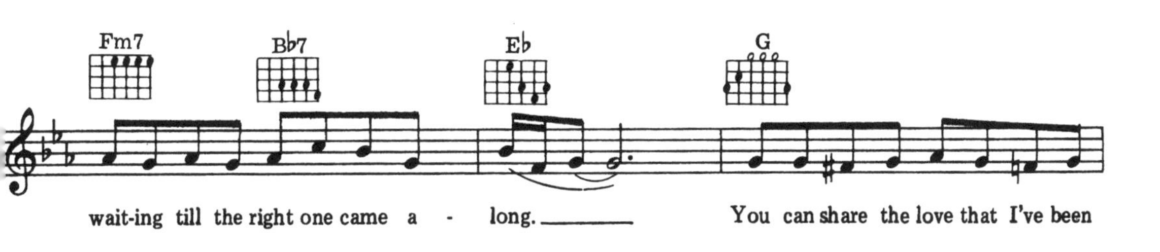
Fm7 B♭7 E♭ G
wait-ing till the right one came a - long.
You can share the love that I've been

Cm Fm7 B♭
D.C.
Repeat to FADE.
keep - ing,
you can put the mu - sic to my song.

Verse 3:

I want to wake up with you,
I want to reach out and know that you're there.
I want you to be the first thing that I see,
I want to wake up with you.

28

HE AIN'T HEAVY, HE'S MY BROTHER

Words by Bob Russell
Music by Bobby Scott

Words and Music by
BOB RUSSELL & BOBBY SCOTT
Slow beat
G D C
The road is long with ma - ny a wind - ing turn,
go his wel - fare is my con- cern,
road from which there is no re -turn,
Am D D#o Em F Am7 Am11 D7
That leads us to who knows where, who knows where. But I'm
No bur- den is he to bear, who'll get there. For I
While we're on the way to there, why not share. And the
G D (7) Em7 Eb
strong, strong e - nough to car - ry him.
know he would not en - cum - ber me.
load does- n't weigh me down at all.
To Coda
G Am7 Am11 G Am7 Am11
He ain't hea- vy he's my bro-ther. So on we
G7 C D7 C
If I'm lad-en at all I'm lad-en with
D7 Bm Dm6 Cmaj7 B7
sad - ness, That ev - 'ry - one's heart is - n't fill'd with the
Em7 G7 C (maj7) A7 Am11
glad-ness of love for one a - noth - er.
D7 D. S. al Coda
It's a long long
CODA
Repeat and Fade
G Am7 Am11
broth-er. Yea, he's my

29
I Will Survive

Words & Music by Dino Fekaris & Freddie Perren

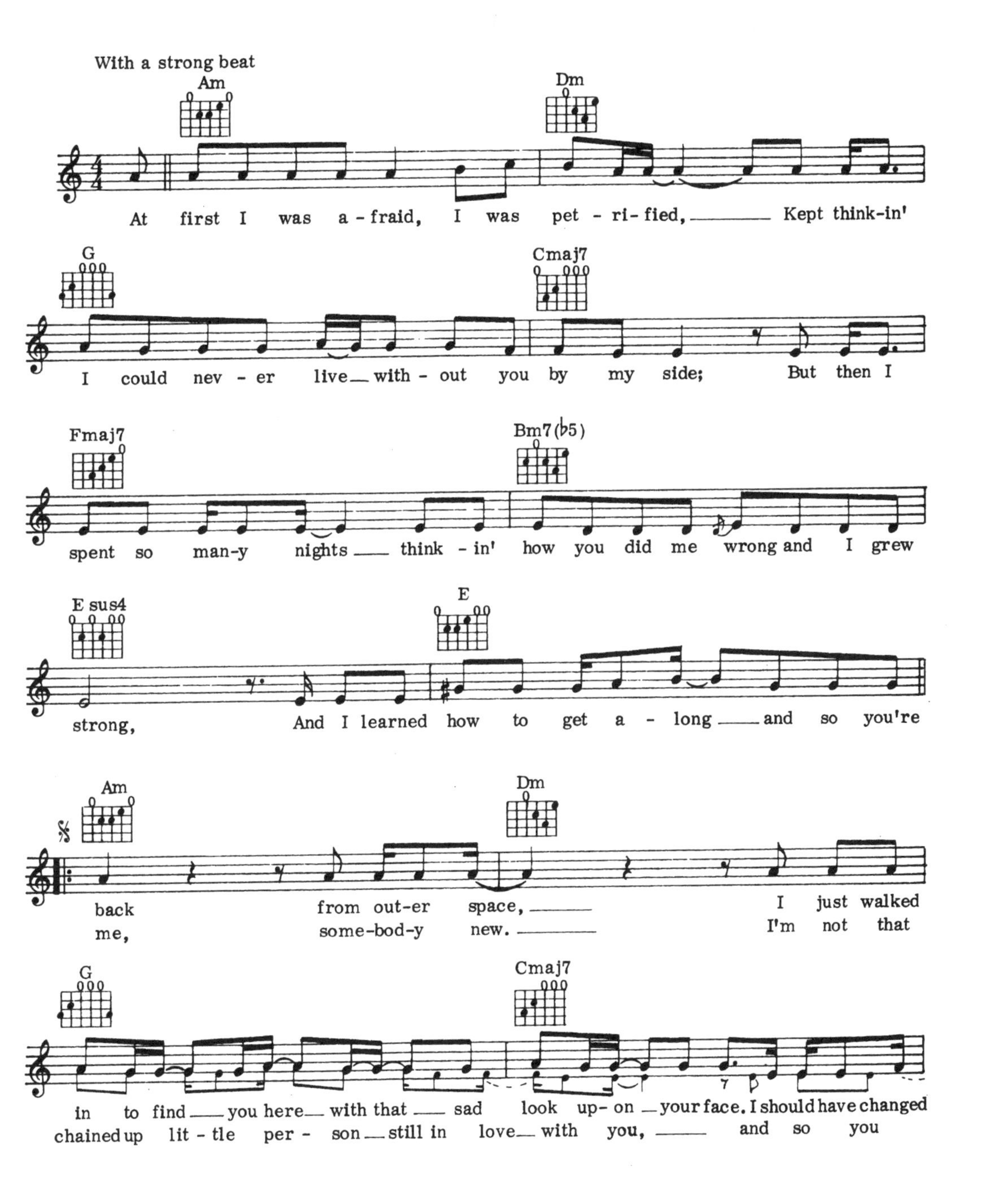
With a strong beat
Am
Dm
At first I was a - fraid, I was pet - ri - fied, Kept think-in'
G
Cmaj7
I could nev - er live with - out you by my side; But then I
Fmaj7
Bm7(♭5)
spent so man-y nights think - in' how you did me wrong and I grew
E sus4
E
strong, And I learned how to get a - long and so you're
Am
Dm
back from out-er space, I just walked
me, some-bod-y new. I'm not that
G
Cmaj7
in to find you here with that sad look up- on your face. I should have changed
chained up lit - tle per - son still in love with you, and so you

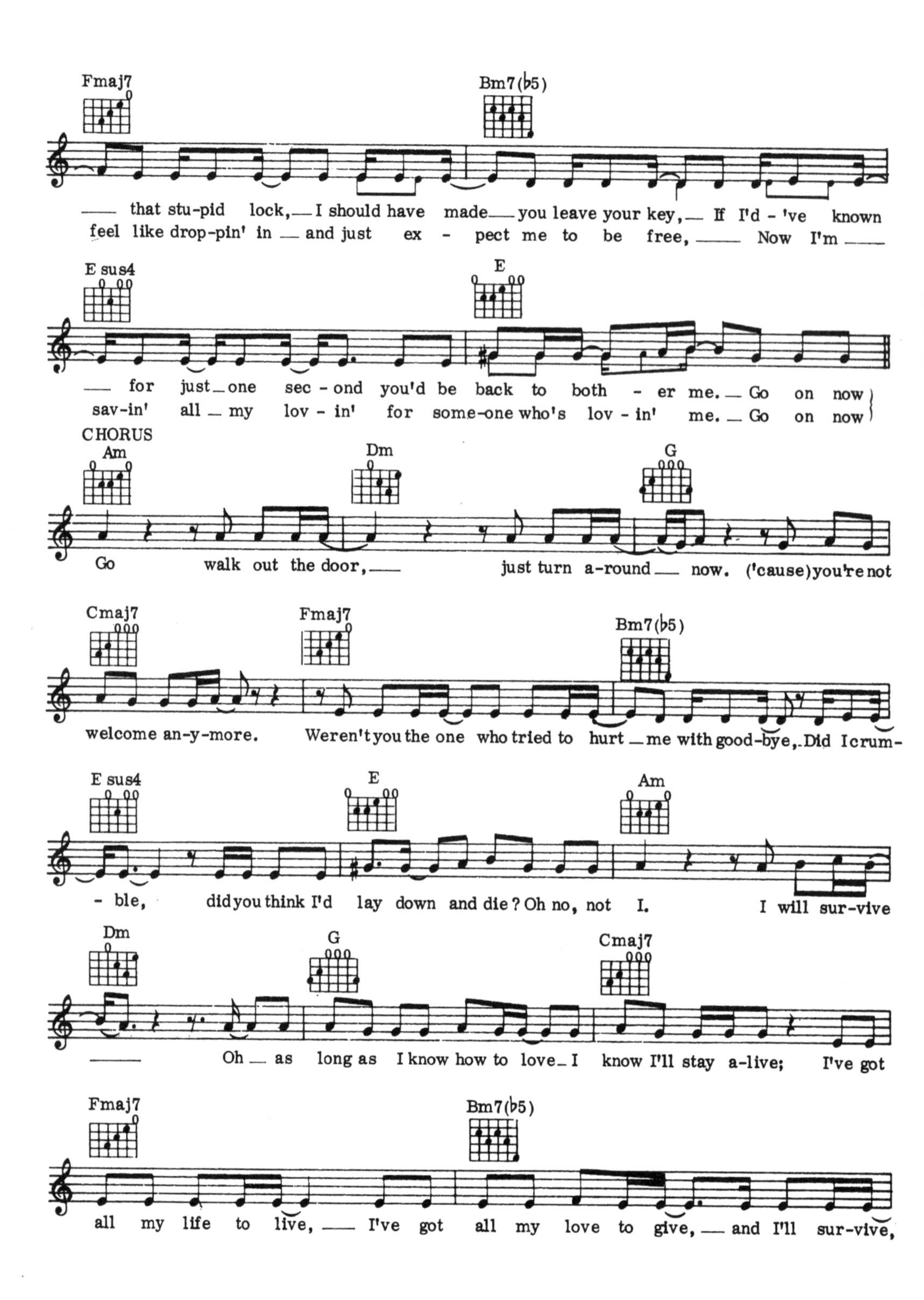
Fmaj7
Bm7(♭5)
— that stu-pid lock, — I should have made — you leave your key, — If I'd - 've known
feel like drop-pin' in — and just ex - pect me to be free, — Now I'm —
E sus4
E
— for just — one sec - ond you'd be back to both - er me. — Go on now
sav-in' all — my lov - in' for some-one who's lov - in' me. — Go on now
CHORUS
Am
Dm
G
Go walk out the door, — just turn a-round — now. ('cause) you're not
Cmaj7
Fmaj7
Bm7(♭5)
welcome an-y-more. Weren't you the one who tried to hurt — me with good-bye, Did I crum-
E sus4
E
Am
- ble, did you think I'd lay down and die? Oh no, not I. I will sur-vive
Dm
G
Cmaj7
— Oh — as long as I know how to love — I know I'll stay a-live; I've got
Fmaj7
Bm7(♭5)
all my life to live, — I've got all my love to give, — and I'll sur-vive,

E sus4
E
Am
To Coda
I will sur-vive. Hey hey.
Dm
G
Cmaj7
Fmaj7
Bm7(♭5)
E sus4
E7
Am
It took all the strength I had not to
Dm
G
fall a - part, Kept try - in' hard to mend the piec - es of my brok-
Cmaj7
Fmaj7
- en heart, And I spent oh so man - y nights just feel - in'
Bm7(♭5)
E sus4
E
D. S. al Coda
sor-ry for my-self. I used to cry but now I hold my head up high and you see
CODA
E
Am
Dm
Am
I'll sur - vive.

30
I'd Like To Teach The World To Sing

Words & Music by Roger Cook, Roger Greenaway, Billy Backer & Billy Davis

Moderato
F G7
I'd like to build the world a home and fur-nish it with love,
C7(sus4) C7 C7(sus4) C7 B♭ C7
Grow ap-ple trees and hon-ey bees and snow-white tur-tle doves. I'd
F G7 C7(sus4) C7
like to teach the world to sing in per-fect har-mo-ny, I'd like to hold it
C7(sus4) C7 B♭ F
in my arms and keep it com-pa-ny. I'd like to see the
G7 C7(sus4) C7
world for once all stand-ing hand in hand, And hear them ech-o
C7(sus4) C7 B♭ F Fine B♭
through the hills for peace through-out the land. That's the song I hear,
F G7 C7 Gm7 C7 Gm7 C7
Let the world sing to-day, A song of peace that ech-oes on and
B♭ F B♭ F C C7
nev-er goes a-way. Put your hand in my hand, let's be-gin to-
F C C7 C11 C7 D.S. al Fine
-day. Put your hand in my hand, help me find the way. I'd

31
I'm Not In Love

Words & Music by Eric Stewart & Graham Gouldman

Moderately
B♭
B♭m
F
I'm not in love, So don't for - get it, It's just a
A7
Dm
B♭
B♭m
sil - ly phase I'm go - ing through. And just be - cause I call you
F
A7
Dm
up, Don't get me wrong, Don't think you've got it made.
B♭
C
C7
F
B♭
I'm not in love, no, no! It's be - cause
B♭11
B♭
B♭m
I like to see you But then a -
F
A7
Dm
gain, That does - n't mean you mean that much to me.
B♭
B♭m
F
So if I call you, Don't make a fuss, Don't tell your

A7
Dm
B♭
friends a-bout the two of us.
I'm not in love, no,
C
C7
F
(no chord)
no!
It's be-cause.
(Instrumental)
F6
Be quiet, Big boys don't cry, Big boys don't cry, Big boys don't cry, Big boys don't cry, Big boys don'
cry, Big boys don't cry.
(Instrumental)
A7
B♭
B♭m
F
I keep your pic-ture up-on the wall, It hides a
A7
Dm
B♭
nas-ty stain that's ly-ing there.
So don't you ask me

Bbm
F
A7
Dm
to give it back.
I know you know it does-n't mean that much to me.
Bb
C9
C7
F
I'm not in love, no, no!
It's be - cause.
Bbm7
Eb7
Ab
Fm7
Bbm7
Ooh, you'll wait a long time for me.
Ooh, you'll
Eb7
F11
1. F7
2. F7
Bb
wait a long time.
I'm not in love,
Bbm
F
A7
Dm
So don't for - get it,
It's just a sil-ly phase I'm go - ing through.
Bb
Bbm
F
And just be - cause
I call you up,
Don't get me
A7
Dm
Bb
wrong, Don't think you've got it made.
I'm not in love,
Bbm
C11
C
I'm not in love.
(Instrumental) 14 times - fade from 13th.

32

IMAGINE

Words & Music by John Lennon

20 bars per minute

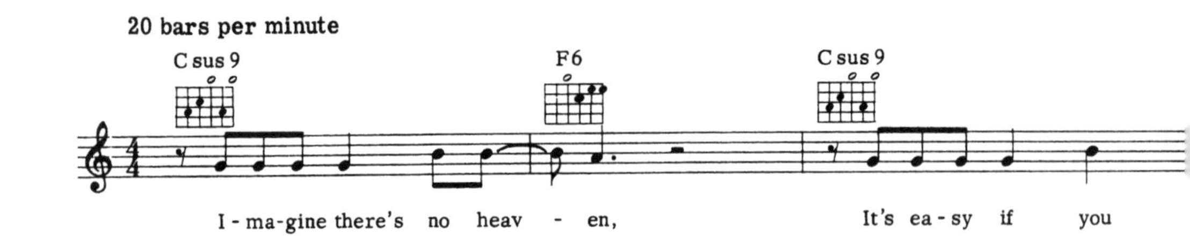
C sus 9
F6
C sus 9
I - ma-gine there's no heav - en,
It's ea - sy if you

F6
C sus 9
F6
try,
No hell
be - low us,

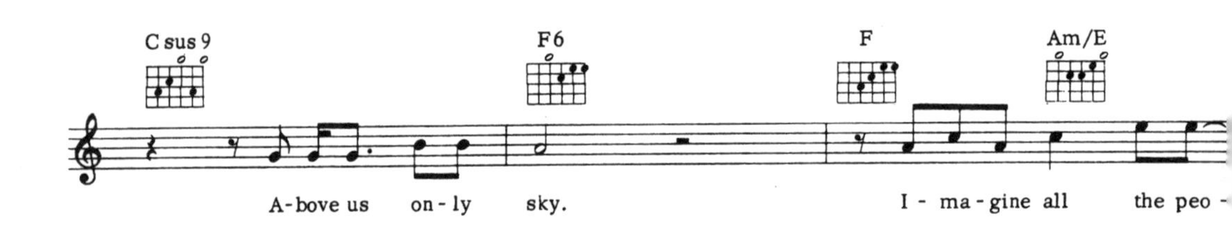
C sus 9
F6
F
Am/E
A-bove us on - ly sky.
I - ma-gine all the peo -

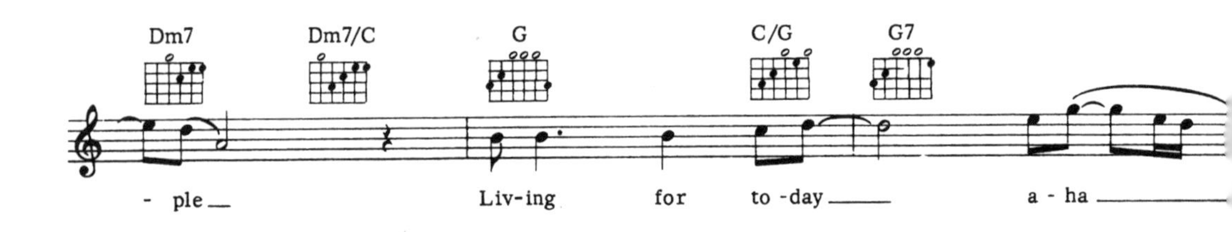
Dm7
Dm7/C
G
C/G
G7
- ple
Liv-ing for to - day
a - ha

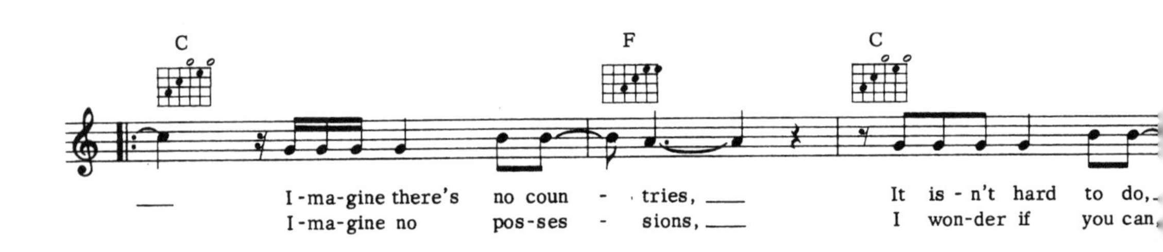
C
F
C
I-ma-gine there's no coun - tries,
It is - n't hard to do,
I-ma-gine no pos-ses - sions,
I won-der if you can,

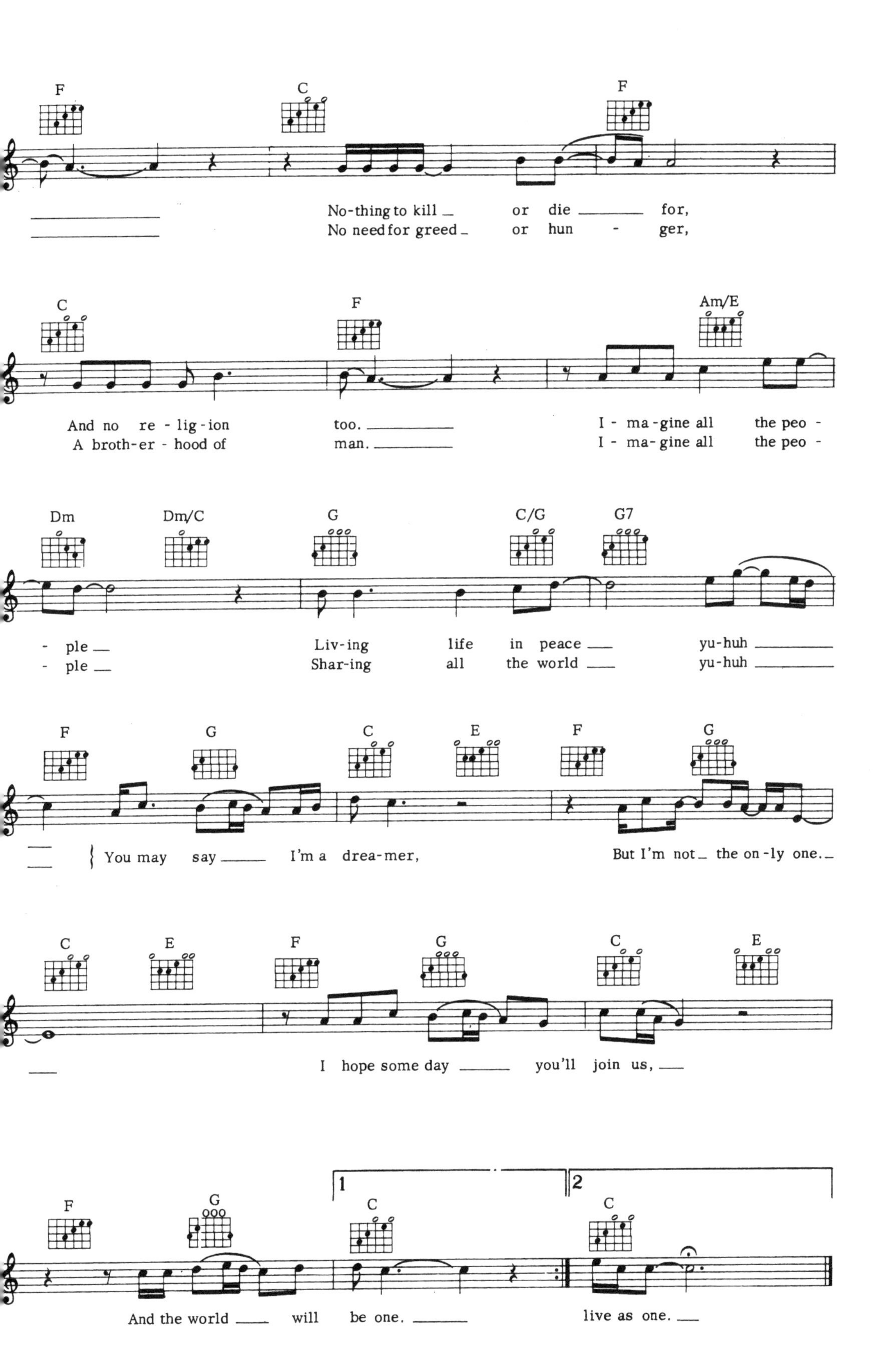
F
C
F
No-thing to kill or die for,
No need for greed or hun - ger,
C
F
Am/E
And no re - lig - ion too.
A broth-er - hood of man.
I - ma - gine all the peo -
I - ma - gine all the peo -
Dm
Dm/C
G
C/G
G7
- ple
- ple
Liv-ing life in peace
Shar-ing all the world
yu-huh
yu-huh
F
G
C
E
F
G
You may say I'm a drea-mer,
But I'm not the on-ly one.
C
E
F
G
C
E
I hope some day you'll join us,
1
2
F
G
C
C
And the world will be one.
live as one.

33

It's Not Unusual

Words & Music by Gordon Mills & Les Reed

Moderately, with a beat
G
Am7
D7
1 It's not un - u - su-al to be loved by an-y-one.
2 It's not un - u - su-al to be out at an-y time.

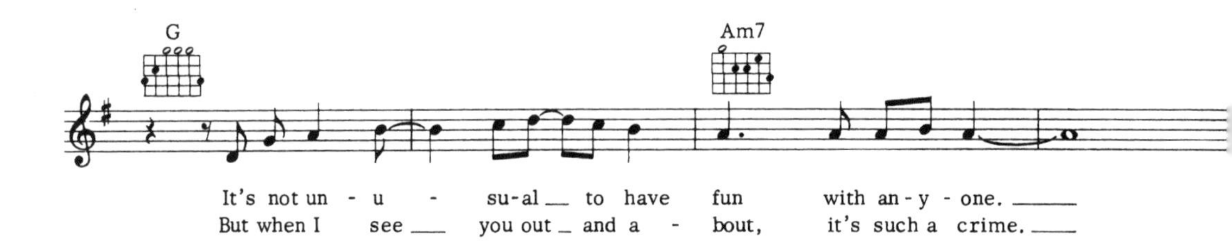
G
Am7
It's not un - u - su-al to have fun with an - y - one.
But when I see you out and a - bout, it's such a crime.

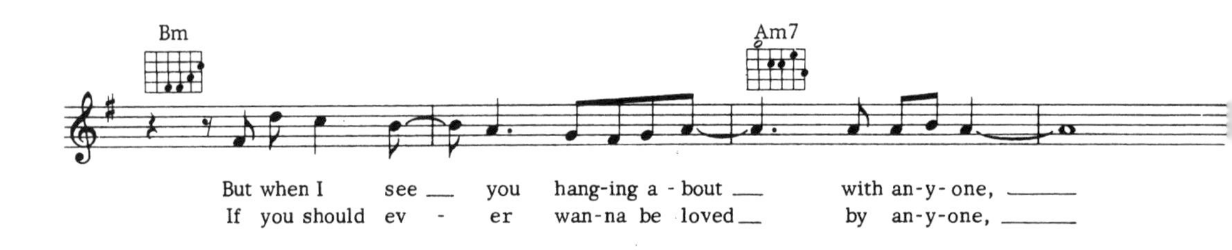
Bm
Am7
But when I see you hang-ing a - bout with an-y- one,
If you should ev - er wan-na be loved by an-y-one,

D7
1
G
D7
It's not un - u - su-al to see me cry. I wan-na die.
It's not un - u - su-al, it

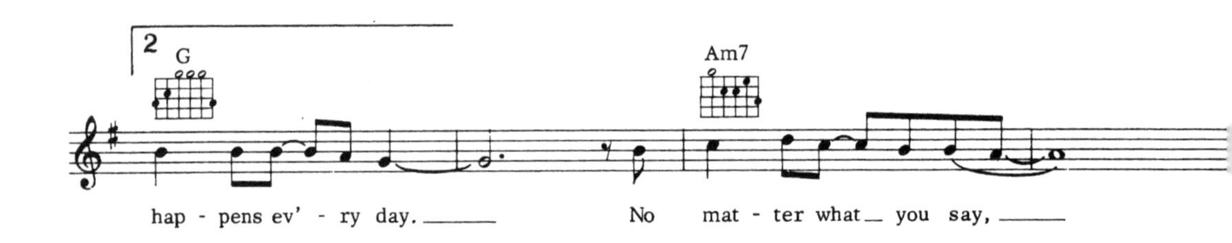
2
G
Am7
hap - pens ev' - ry day. No mat - ter what you say,

D7
G
you'll find it hap - pens all the time.
G
Am7
Love will nev - er do
what you want it to.
D7
Bm7
B♭7
Am7
D7
Why can't this cra - zy love be mine?
G
Am7
D7
It's not un - u - su - al to be mad with an - y - one.
G
Am7
Bm
It's not un - u - su - al to be sad with an - y - one.
But if I ev -
Am7
D7
- er find that you've changed at an - y time.
It's not un - u -
G
Am7
D9
G
- su - al to find that I'm in love with you.

Itsy Bitsy, Teenie Weenie, Yellow Polkadot Bikini

Words & Music by Lee Pockriss & Paul J. Vance

Moderato

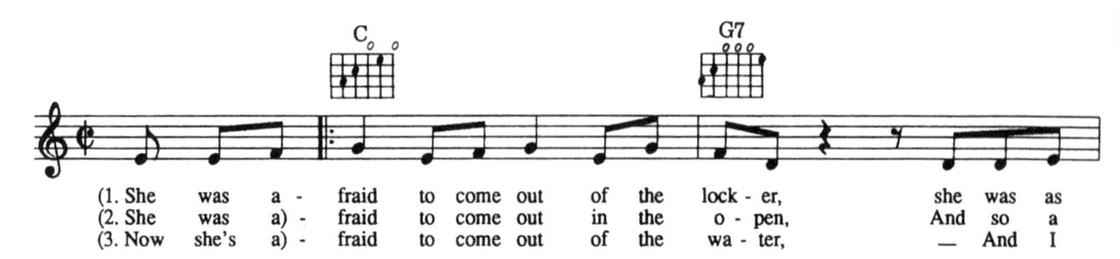
C
G7
(1. She was a - fraid to come out of the lock - er, she was as
(2. She was a) - fraid to come out in the o - pen, And so a
(3. Now she's a) - fraid to come out of the wa - ter, — And I

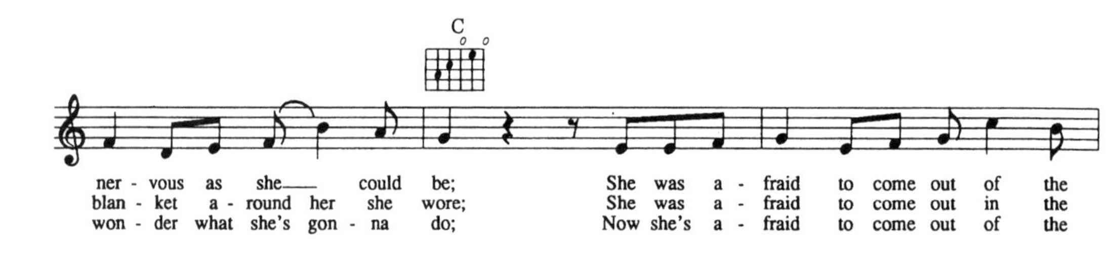
C
ner - vous as she could be; She was a - fraid to come out of the
blan - ket a - round her she wore; She was a - fraid to come out in the
won - der what she's gon - na do; Now she's a - fraid to come out of the

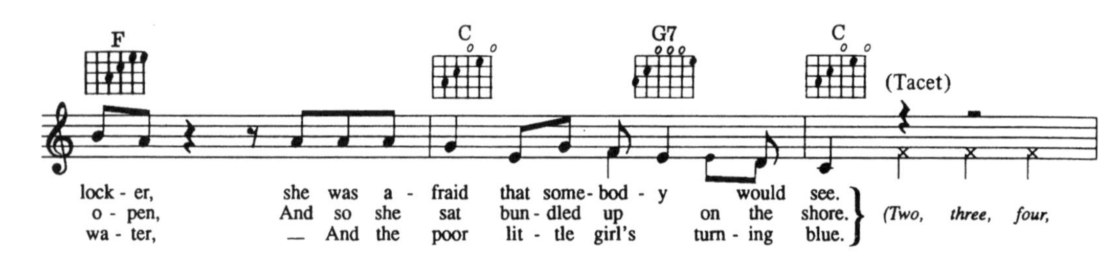
F
C
G7
C
(Tacet)
lock - er, she was a - fraid that some - bod - y would see.
o - pen, And so she sat bun - dled up on the shore.
wa - ter, — And the poor lit - tle girl's turn - ing blue.
(Two, three, four,

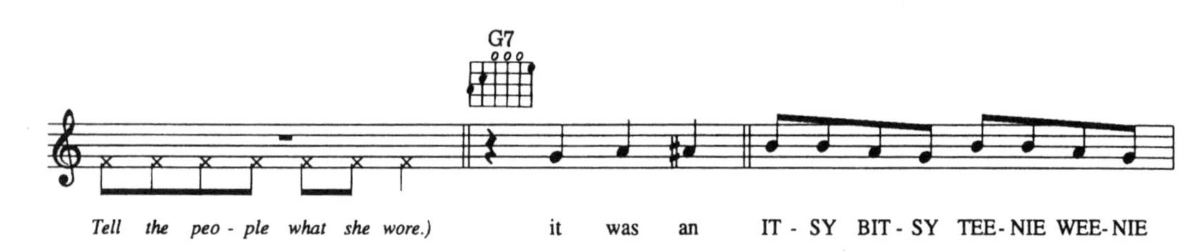
G7
Tell the peo - ple what she wore.) it was an IT - SY BIT - SY TEE - NIE WEE - NIE

C G7 C
YEL - LOW POL - KA - DOT BI - KI - NI, That she wore for the first time to - day. An
G7 C G7
IT - SY BIT - SY TEE - NIE WEE - NIE YEL - LOW POL - KA - DOT BI - KI - NI, so in the
1. lock - er
2. blan - ket
3. wa - ter
she
1, 2
C (Tacet)
wan - ted to stay. (Two, three, four, Stick a - round. we'll tell you more.
2. She was a –
3. Now she's a –
3
C G7
want - ed to stay. From the lock - er to the blan - ket,
C
From the blan - ket to the shore; From the shore to the
G7 C
wa - ter, Guess there is - n't an - y more.

35
If You Leave Me Now

Words & Music by Peter Cetera

Moderately Slow
Bbmaj7
Gm7
1. If you leave me now, you'll take a - way the big - gest part
leave me now, you'll take a - way the ver - y heart
Dm7
Gm7
C7
of me. Ooh no, ba - by, please
of me. Ooh no, ba - by, please
F
1
Bb
F
Bb
2
Bb
don't go. 2. And if you Ooh,
Gm7
C7
F
Bb
F
Bb
girl, I just want you to stay.
Eb9
Ebm7
Abm
A love like ours is love that's hard to find.
We've come too far to leave it all be-hind.

Eb
Gm7
Eb
How could we let it slip a-way.
How could we end it all this way?
1
Bb
G sus/Bb
D7
2
Bb
When to-mor-
Dm7
Gm7
Cm
Dm
-row comes, then we'll re-gret the things we said to-day.
Ebm
To Coda
F7-9
Bbmaj7
Gm7
Dm7
Gm7
C
F
Bb
Gm7
C7
F
Bb
F
Eb
D. S. al Coda
(with rpts)

CODA
E♭m
B♭maj7
Gm7
If you leave me now, you'll take a-way the big - gest part
Dm7
of me.
Gm7
C7
Ooh, no, ba - by, please
F
B♭
don't go.
Gm7
C7
F
B♭
F/B♭
B♭
F/B♭
B♭
F/B♭
B♭
Gm7
C7
Ooh, girl, I've
Sweet ma - ma, just
F
B♭
got to have you by my side.
got to have your love in-side me.
Gm7
C7
F
B♭
F/B♭
B♭
F/B♭
B♭
F/B♭
B♭
Repeat & fade.
Ooh

JAILHOUSE ROCK

Words & Music by Jerry Leiber & Mike Stoller

F6
E7
The war-den threw a par-ty in the Coun-ty jail, The
Spi-der Mur-phy play'd the ten-or sax-o-phone,
F6
E7
pri-son band was there and they be-gan to wail, The
Lit-tle Joe was blow-in' on the slide trom-bone, The
F6
F7
band was jump-in' and the joint be-gan to swing. You
drum-mer boy from Il-li-nois went crash, boom, bang' The
F6
CHORUS
B♭7
should-'ve heard those knocked out jail-birds sing.
whole rhy-thm sec-tion was the Pur-ple Gang.
Let's Rock'
F6
B♭7
Let's Rock!
Ev-'ry-bo-dy in the whole cell block
F6
B♭6
F6
1
2
F7
Was a-dan-cin' to the jail-house Rock!

37

JEALOUS GUY

Words & Music by John Lennon

♩ = 80
G
Em
D
D7
Em
G
Em
D
1. I was dreaming of the past
2. I was feel-ing in - se-cure
3. (Whistle)
4. I was trying to catch your eyes
D7
Em
and my heart was beat-ing fast
you might not love me an - y more
thought that you was try-ing to hide
Em6
D
I be- gan to lose con-trol
I was shiv - er - ing in-side
I was swal - low - ing my pain

Em
C
I be-gan— to lose— con - trol.
I was shiv— er-ing— in - side.
I was swal— low-ing— my pain.
G
Dm
C
D7
G
Dm
I did-n-t mean to hurt— you
I'm sor-ry that— I
B♭
G
made you cry—
Oh no
I did-n't mean— to hurt—
3
Em
G6
1.2.3.
C
G
you
I'm just a jeal-ous guy.
4
C
G
C
G
I'm just a jealous guy
watch out
I'm just a jealous guy— look out-babe—
C
G
I'm just a jeal - ous guy.

38

(JUST LIKE) STARTING OVER

Words & Music by John Lennon

Freely
A A+ F♯m/A A+
Our life together is so precious together. We have
A E7 A E7 A A+
grown. We have grown. Although our love is still special.
F♯m/A A7 D/A Dm/A A
Let's take a chance and fly away somewhere alone. It's
Moderately, with a strong beat
A A+
been too long since we took the time. No one's to blame; I know time flies so
day we used to make it, love. Why can't we be makin' love nice and
Bm E Bm E
Instrumental
quickly! But when I see you, darling,
easy? It's time to spread our wings and
C♯m F♯ Bm E
It's like we both are falling in love again.
fly. Don't let another day go by, my love.
It'll be just
A A+ A
to coda
like starting over, starting over.

1
A+
Ev'-ry
2
G
tacet
Why don't we take off a -
Am
D7
G
lone,
take a trip some-where far, far a-way.
Em
Am
D7
We'll be to - geth - er all a - lone a - gain, like we
D.S. (1st lyric) al coda
G
E
D/F♯
E/G♯
used to in the ear-ly days.
Well, well, dar - ling, It's (been)
CODA
A+
A
A+
Our life to -geth-er is so
F♯m/A
A+
A
E
pre-cious to -geth-er.
We have grown.
A
E
A
We have grown.
Al - though our love is still
A+
F♯m/A
A7
D
spe-cial,
Let's take a chance and fly a - way
Dm
A
A+
repeat (vocal ad lib.) and fade
some - where.
Instrumental

39

KARMA CHAMELEON

Words & Music by George O'Dowd, Jonathan Moss, Roy Hay, Michael Craig & Philip Pickett

Moderato
mf
B♭ F B♭
De- sert lov- ing in your eyes all the way.
2. Hear your wick- ed words ev - 'ry day.
F B♭
If I lis- ten to your lies would you say.
And you used to be so sweet I heard you say.
E♭ F
I'm a man with- out con - vic - tion,
That my love was an a - ddic - tion,
E♭ F
I'm a man who does - n't know,
When we cling our love is strong,
E♭ F
How to sell a con - tra - dic - tion,
When you go you're gone for - ev - er,
Cm7 Gm F
You come and go, You come and go.
You string a - long, You string a - long.

CHORUS
B♭
F
Gm7
Kar-ma kar-ma kar-ma kar-ma kar-ma cha-me - le - on,
Cm7
B♭
You come and go, You come and go,
F
B♭
Dm7
Lov-ing would be ea-sy if your col-ours were like my
Gm7
Cm7
dream, Red gold and green, Red gold and
1
B♭
F
2
B♭
F
green. 2. Did-n't green.
E♭
Dm7
Ev-'ry day is like sur-vi - val,
Cm7
Gm7
1
2
F
D.S. to fade
You're my lov - er, Not my ri - val. val.

Killing Me Softly With His Song

Words by Norman Gimbel
Music by Charles Fox

Tempo Rubato
Fm
Db
Eb7
Strum-ming my pain with his fin - gers, sing-ing my life with his words

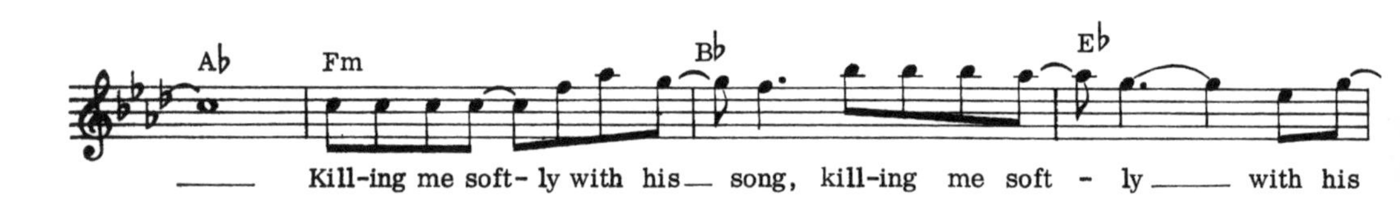
Ab
Fm
Bb
Eb
Kill-ing me soft- ly with his song, kill-ing me soft - ly with his

Db
Ab
Db
Fm
F sus4
song. Tell-ing my whole life with his words, kill-ing me soft - ly

A tempo ♩ = 108
F
Eb7 sus4
Eb7
Bbm7
with his song.
I heard he sang
I felt all flushed
He sang as if

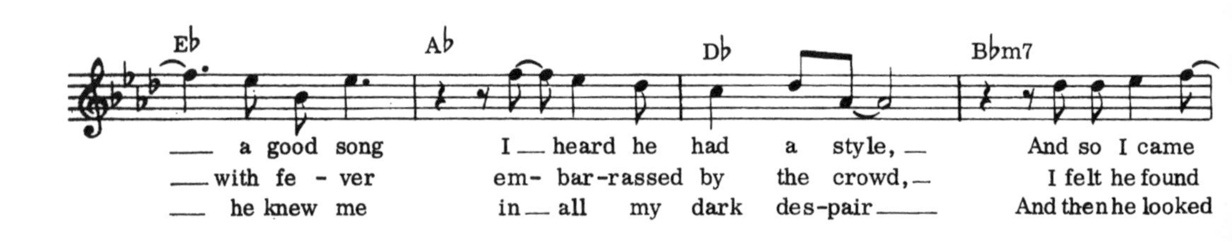
Eb
Ab
Db
Bbm7
a good song I heard he had a style, And so I came
with fe - ver em- bar-rassed by the crowd, I felt he found
he knew me in all my dark des-pair And then he looked

Eb
Fm
C7sus4 Fm Bbm7
to see him and list - en for a while.
And there he was
my let - ters and read each one out loud.
I prayed that he
right through me as if I was - n't there.
But he was there
Eb7
Ab
C7
Fm
this young boy a stran-ger to my eyes
would fin - ish but he just kept right on
Strum-ming my pain with his fin-
this stran - ger sing - ing clear and strong
Bbm
Eb7
Fm
- gers, sing-ing my life with his words
Kill-ing me soft - ly with his
Bb
Eb
Db
Ab
song, kill-ing me soft - ly with his song, tell-ing my whole life with his
Db
Gb
To Coda
F
words, Kill-ing me soft - ly with his song.
1.2.
3.
Fm
Bbm
He was strum-ming there yea he was sing-
Eb
Ab
Fm
D. S. al Coda
CODA
F
- ing my life, Kill-ing me soft- ly with his

41

Knowing Me, Knowing You

Words & Music by Benny Andersson, Björn Ulvaeus & Stig Anderson

Moderato

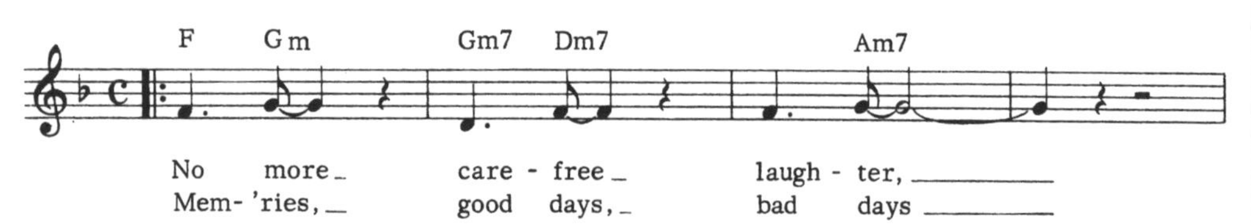

F Gm Gm7 Dm7 Am7
No more_ care - free_ laugh - ter,
Mem- 'ries,_ good days,_ bad days

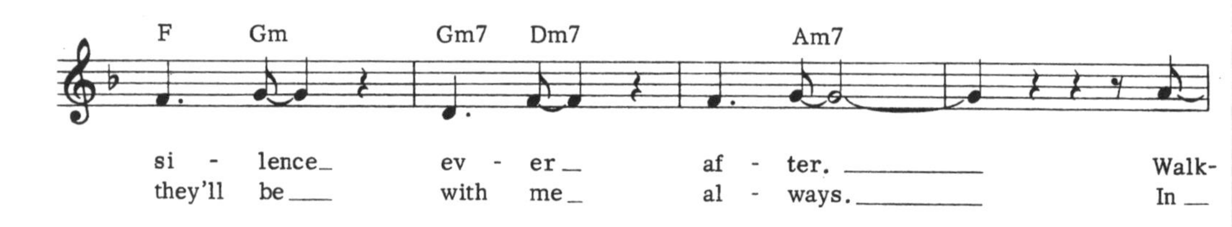

F Gm Gm7 Dm7 Am7
si - lence_ ev - er_ af - ter. Walk-
they'll be_ with me_ al - ways. In_

Dm C
- ing thro' an em-pty house,_ tears in my eyes ;_
_ these old fa - mil-iar rooms_ chil-dren would play ;_

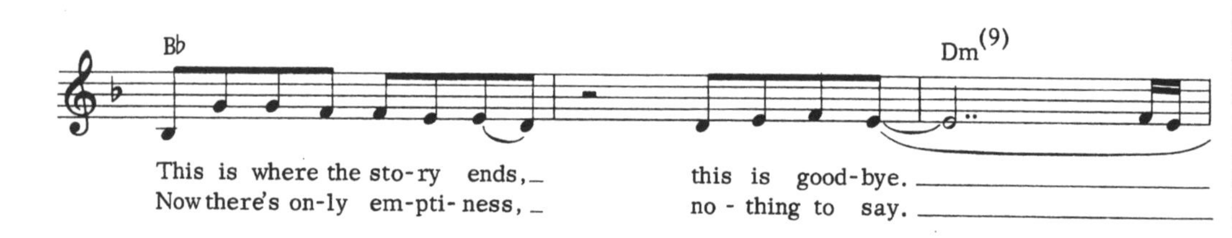

B♭ Dm(9)
This is where the sto-ry ends,_ this is good-bye.
Now there's on-ly em-pti-ness,_ no - thing to say.

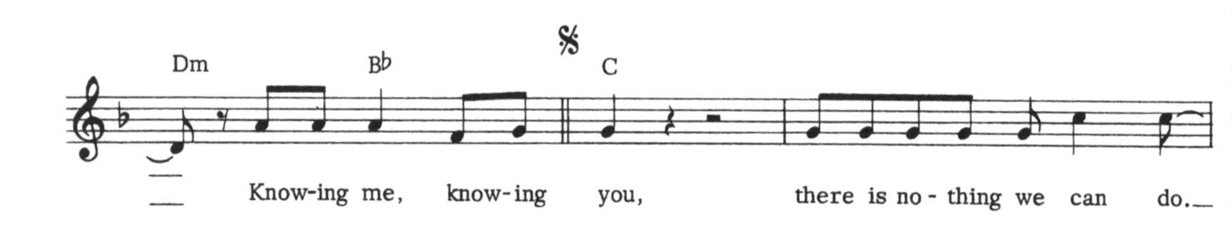

Dm B♭ 𝄋 C
Know-ing me, know-ing you, there is no - thing we can do._

F
Bb
C
Knowing me, knowing you, we just have to face it; this time
F Bb C F Am Bb C
we're through. Breaking up is never easy, I know, but I
F Bb C F Bbma7 C
To Coda
have to go. Knowing me, knowing you, it's the best I can
[Instrumental]
F Dm Am Bb C
do.
F Dm Am Bb C
D.S. al
C Dm C Dm Bb
Knowing me, knowing
CODA
F Dm Am Bb C
repeat to fade
do.

42

THE LADY IN RED

Words & Music by Chris de Burgh

Moderato
INTRO
B♭
/D
E♭maj7
F
VERSE
B♭
E♭maj7
1. I've never seen you looking so lovely as you did tonight,
never seen you looking so gorgeous as you did tonight,
F9
D7
D/F♯
Gm
I've never seen you shine so bright,
I've never seen you shine so bright,
F
E♭
mm mm mm mm.
you were amazing.
I've
I've
B♭
E♭maj7
never seen so many men ask you if you wanted to dance,
never seen so many people want to be there by your side,
F9
D7
D/F♯
Gm
they're looking for a little romance,
and when you turned to me and smiled,
it

B♭7/F
E♭
giv - en half a chance,
and I have
took my breath a - way,
and I have
Cm
nev - er seen that dress you're wear - ing,
or the
nev - er had such a feel - ing,
such a
F7
high - lights in your hair that catch your eyes,
feel - ing of com - plete and ut - ter love,
Gm
F
CHORUS
I have been blind.
as I do to - night.
The
F/E♭
B♭
B♭maj7/D
la - dy in red
E♭9
F
Gm
F/A
is danc - ing with me,
cheek to cheek,

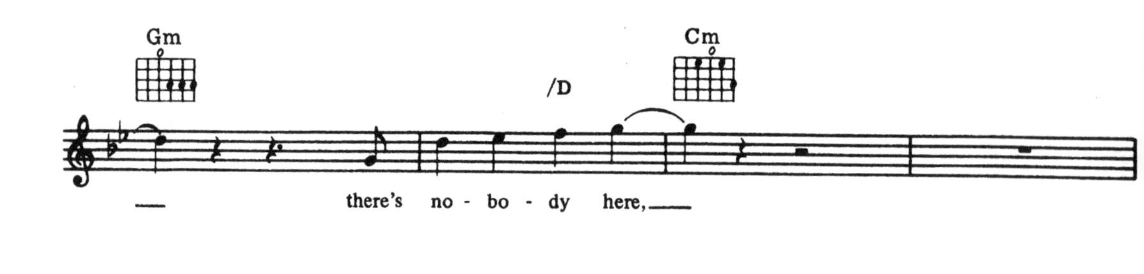
Gm
/D
Cm
there's no - bo - dy here,

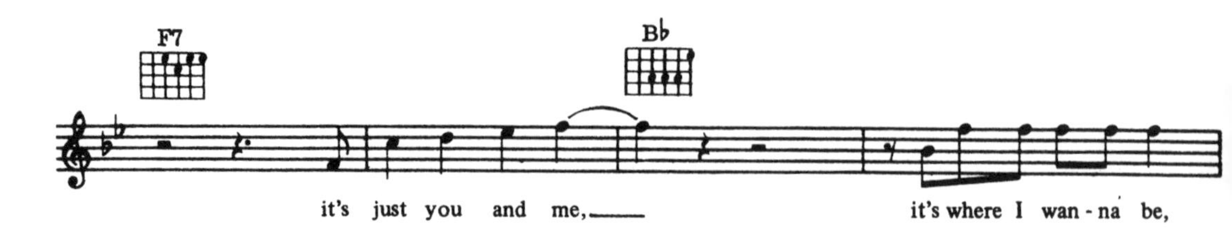
F7
Bb
it's just you and me,
it's where I wan - na be,

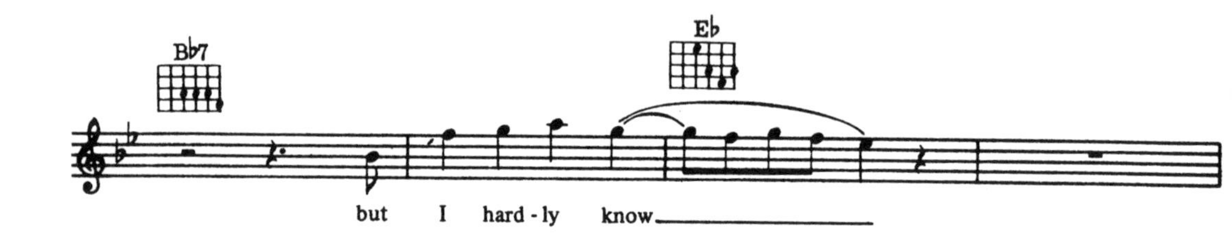
Bb7
Eb
but I hard - ly know

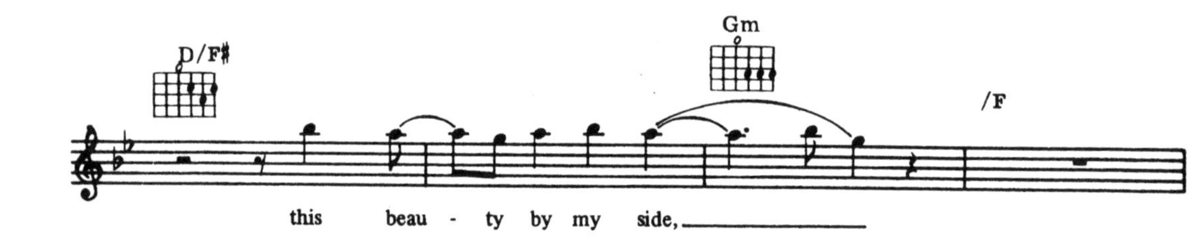
D/F#
Gm
/F
this beau - ty by my side,

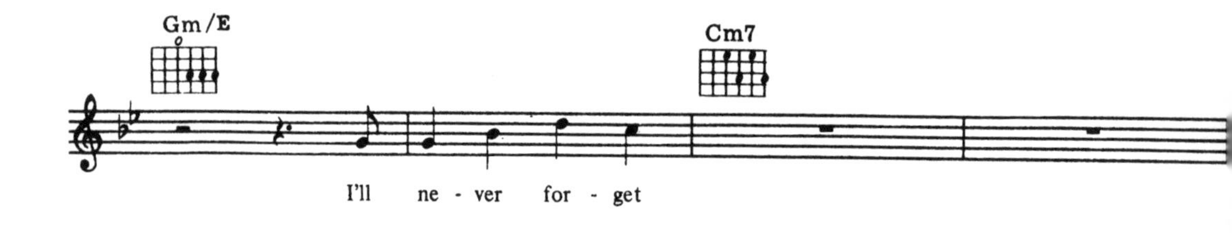
Gm/E
Cm7
I'll ne - ver for - get

F
1.
Bb
/D
the way you look to - night.

Ebmaj7
Bb
/D
Ebmaj7
F
2.
Gm
2. I've way you look to - night,
Gm
/E
Cm7
I nev - er will for - get
F7
Bb
the way you look to - night.
/D
Ebmaj7
F
Bb
x3
The la - dy in red,
Bb/D
Ebmaj7
F
Bb
my la - dy in red.

MAMMA MIA

Words & Music by Benny Andersson, Björn Ulvaeus & Stig Anderson

D D+ D D+
D A D G
I've been cheat-ed by you since I don't know when,
I've been ang-ry and sad a-bout things that you do,
D A D
So I made up my mind it must come to an end.
I can't count all the times that I've told you we're through.
G D D+
Look at me now, will I ev-er learn,
And when you go, when you slam the door,
D D+ G
I don't know how, But I sud-den-ly lose con-trol,
I think you know, that you won't be a-way too long,
A G D
there's a fi-re with-in my soul. Just a
you know that I'm not that strong. Just a
A G D A
look and I can hear a bell ring, One more look and I for-get ev-'ry-thing.
look and I can hear a bell ring, One more look and I for-get ev-'ry-thing.

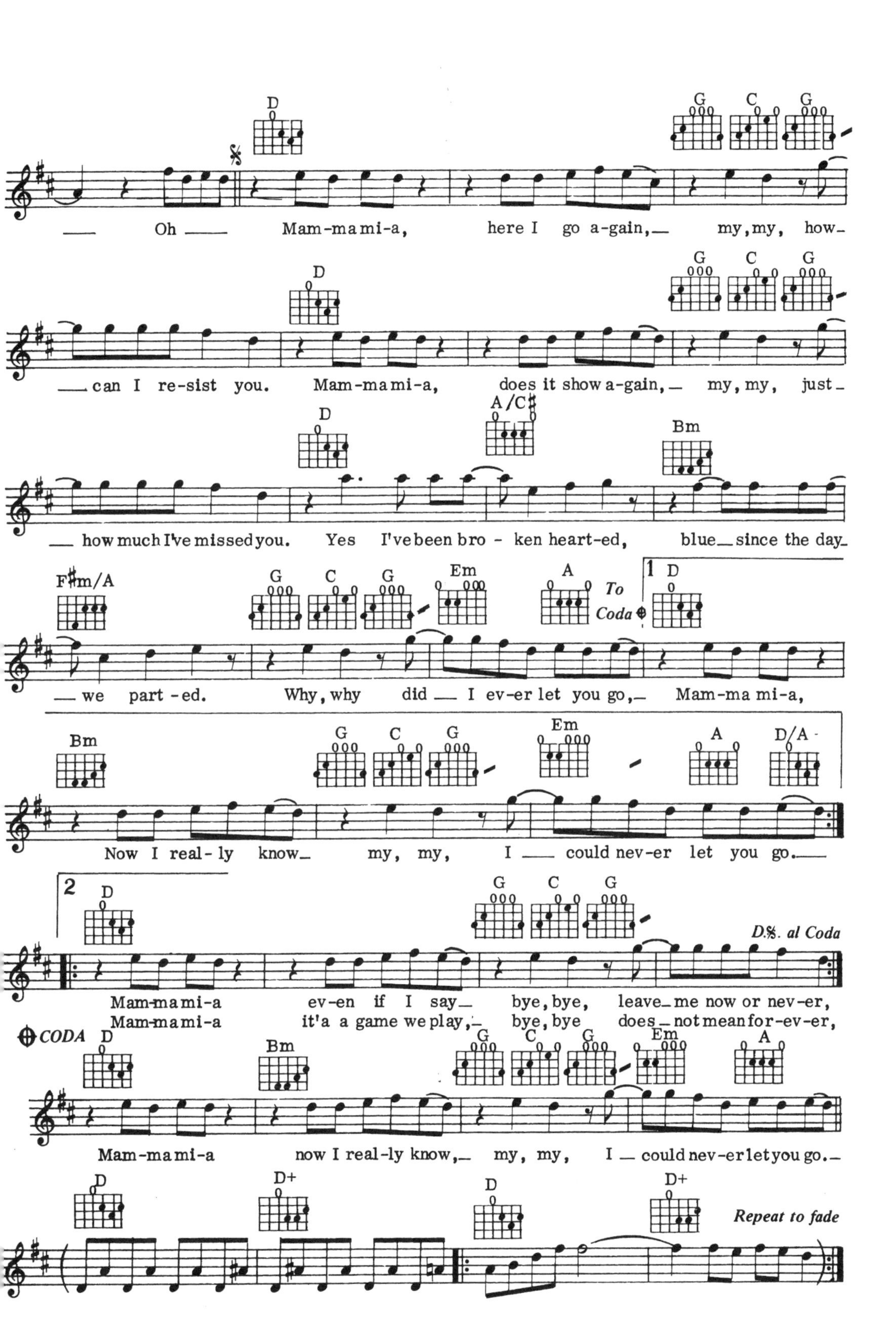
D G C G
Oh Mam-ma mi-a, here I go a-gain, my, my, how
D G C G
can I re-sist you. Mam-ma mi-a, does it show a-gain, my, my, just
D A/C♯ Bm
how much I've missed you. Yes I've been bro - ken heart-ed, blue since the day
F♯m/A G C G Em A To Coda 1 D
we part-ed. Why, why did I ev-er let you go, Mam-ma mi-a,
Bm G C G Em A D/A
Now I real-ly know my, my, I could nev-er let you go.
2 D G C G
D.S. al Coda
Mam-ma mi-a ev-en if I say bye, bye, leave me now or nev-er,
Mam-ma mi-a it'a a game we play, bye, bye does not mean for-ev-er,
CODA D Bm G C G Em A
Mam-ma mi-a now I real-ly know, my, my, I could nev-er let you go.
D D+ D D+
Repeat to fade

44

Love Is All Around

Words & Music by Reg Presley

♩= 85
B♭ Cm E♭ F
1. I feel it in my fin - gers, I feel it in my toes.
(See lyrics 2)
B♭ Cm E♭ F B♭ Cm
The love that's all a - round me,
E♭ F B♭ Cm E♭ F
And so the feel - ing grows. It's
B♭ Cm E♭ F B♭ Cm
writ - ten on the wind, It's ev - 'ry - where I go,
E♭ F B♭ Cm E♭ F
So if you real - ly love me, Come on and let it show.

B♭
Cm
E♭
F
E♭
Cm
E♭
You know I love you, I al-ways— will,— My mind's made up by the
B♭
E♭
Cm
way that I feel,— There's no be - gin - ning, There'll be no— end,— 'Cause
F
1.
F7
on my— love— you can de - pend.
B♭
Cm
E♭
Fsus4
F
B♭
Cm
E♭
F
Fsus4
2. I
2.
F7
B♭/F
F
B♭/F
F7
Got to keep it mov - ing. It's
3f

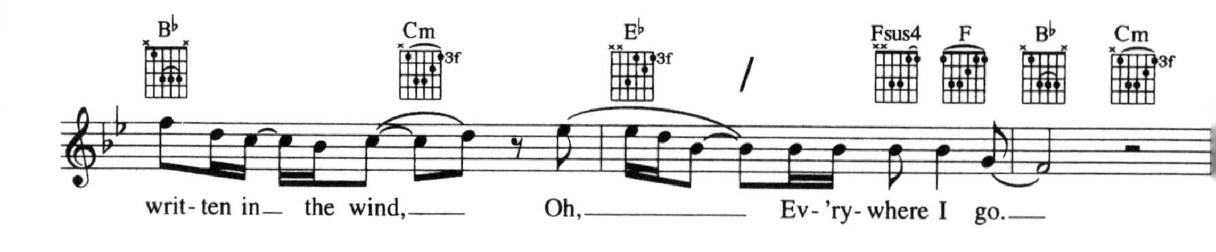
B♭ Cm E♭ Fsus4 F B♭ Cm
writ-ten in the wind, Oh, Ev-'ry-where I go.

E♭ Fsus4 F B♭ Cm E♭ Fsus4 F
So if you real - ly love me, Come on and let it

B♭ Cm E♭ F B♭ Cm
show. Come on and let it Come on and let it,
show.)

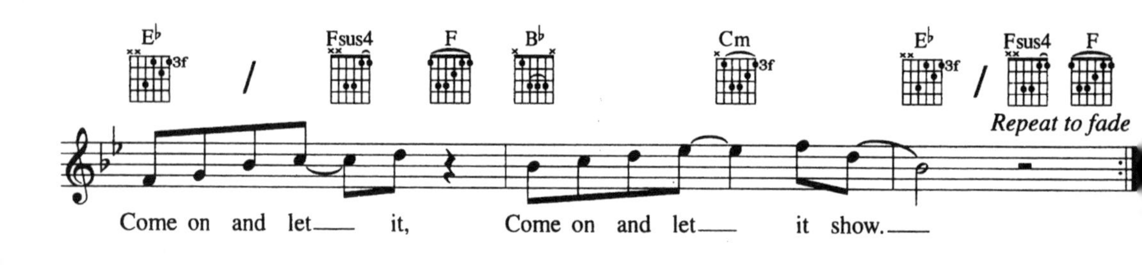
E♭ Fsus4 F B♭ Cm E♭ Fsus4 F
Repeat to fade
Come on and let it, Come on and let it show.

2. I see your face before me
As I lay on my bed,
I cannot get to thinking
Of all the things you said.
You gave your promise to me
And I gave mine to you,
I need someone beside me
In everything I do.

45
MASSACHUSETTS

Words & Music by Barry Gibb, Robin Gibb & Maurice Gibb

Moderato
G Am C G
Feel I'm go - ing back ___ to Mas - sa - chu - setts;
Tried to hitch a ride ___ to San Fran - cis - co;
Talk a - bout the life ___ in Mas - sa - chu - setts;
Am C
some - thing's tell - ing me ___ I must go
got - ta do the things ___ I wan - na
speak a - bout the peo - ple I have
G
home. _ And the lights all went out in Mas - sa -
do. ___ And the lights all went out in Mas - sa -
seen. _ And the lights all went out in Mas - sa -
C G
chu - setts the day I left her
chu - setts; they brought me back to
chu - setts; and Mas - sa - chu - setts is
D G 1. 2. D 3. Am C
stand - ing on her own.
see my way with you.
one place I have seen.
Repeat and fade
G Am C G Am C
I will re - mem - ber Mas - sa - chu - setts.

MERRY XMAS EVERYBODY

Words & Music by Neville Holder & James Lea

Medium shuffle
G
Em7
Bm
mf
Are you hang - ing up a stock - ing on your wall?
- ing for the fam - 'ly to ar - rive?
- ing up a stock - ing on your wall?
D7
C9
D7
G
Em7
Bm
It's the time that ev - 'ry San - ta has a ball.
Are you sure you got the room to spare in - side?
Are you hop - ing that the snow will start to fall?
D7
Am7
D7
C
G
Does he ride a red nosed rein - deer? Does a ton -
Does your gran - ny al - ways tell ya that the old
Do you ride on down the hill - side in a bug -
C
G
Am7
up on his sleigh? Do the fair - ies keep him so -
songs are the best? Then she's up and rock 'n' roll -
gy you have made? When you land up - on your head
D7
al Coda
f
ber for a day?
in' with the best!
then you bin slayed!
So hear it
G
Bm7
B♭
is, Mer - ry Christ - mas, Ev - 'ry - bo - dy's hav - ing fun,

D7
G
Bm7
Look to the fu - ture now, It's
B♭
D7
1
on - ly just be - gun.
Are you wait-
2
INTERLUDE
Dm
B♭
What will your dad-dy do when he sees your mam-
Dm
B♭
C
D7
D. S. al Coda
ma kis-sin' San - ta Claus? Ah ah!
Are you hang-
CODA
G
Bm7
B♭
is, Mer-ry Christ - mas, Ev-'ry-bo - dy's hav-ing fun.
D7
G
Bm7
Look to the fu - ture now, It's
1
B♭
D
on - ly just be - gun.
So here it
2
B♭
D
on - ly just be - gun.

47

MESSAGE IN A BOTTLE

Words & Music by Sting

Fast
C#m9 Amaj7 B7 F#m C#m9 Amaj7 B7
1. Just a cast - a - way, an is-land lost at sea-
2. A year has passed since I wrote my note
% Walked out this morn-ing, I don't be - lieve what I
F#m C#m9 Amaj7 B7 F#m C#m9 Amaj7 B7
- - o, a-nuzz-er lone - ly day, no-one here but me-
but I should have known this right from the start,
saw, a hun-dred bil-lion bot-tles washed up on the shore.
F#m C#m9 Amaj7 B7 F#m C#m9 Amaj7 B7
- o, More lone - li - ness than an - y man could bear.
Only hope can keep me to-geth - er
Seems like I'm not alone in being a - lone
F#m C#m9 Amaj7 B7 F#m C#m9 Amaj7 B7
Res - cue me be - fore I fall in - to des - pair.
Love can mend your life but love can break your heart.
A hundred bil - lion cast - a - ways look - ing for a home.
F#m A D E A D
o. I'll send an S O S to the world, I'll send an S-
E F#m D F#m
O S to the world I hope that some-one gets my, I hope that some-

D
F♯m
D
C♯m
- one gets_my, I hope_that some-one gets_my_ mes-sage in_ a bot-
A
C♯m
A
To Coda
C♯m
- tle,_ yeah, mes-sage in_ a bot-
A
1
F♯m
2
F♯m
- tle,_ yeah.
D.%. al Coda
CODA
C♯m
A
mes-sage in_a bot - tle,_
C♯m
A
C♯m
A
mes-sage in_ a bot - tle,_oh yeah.
F♯m
C♯m9
Amaj7
B7
F♯m
Repeat to fade
C♯m9
Amaj7
B7
F♯m
C♯m9
F♯m
I'm send-ing out_ an S_ O_ S,_ I'm

MISTLETOE AND WINE

Words by Leslie Stewart & Jeremy Paul
Music by Keith Strachan

Easy relaxed tempo
B♭
F7
B♭
F7
B♭
Gm
The child is a— king, the car - oll - ers— sing, The old is
F
F7
E♭
passed, there's a new —— be - gin-ning. Dreams of San - ta,
B♭
C7
F7
dreams of snow, Fin - gers numb, fac - es a - glow. It's
B♭
Christ - mas time, mis-tle-toe and wine, Child - ren
E♭
B♭
F
F7
sing - ing Chris - ti-an rhyme With logs on the fire — and

B♭
gifts on the tree; A time to re - joice in the good that we

B♭
see. 2. A time for liv-ing, a time for be-liev-ing, A
3. It's a time for giv-ing, a time for get-ting, A
Gm E♭ Gm F F7
time for trust-ing, not de-ceiv-ing.
time for for-giv-ing, and for for-get-ting.
E♭ B♭
Love and laugh-ter and joy ev-er af-ter;
Christ-mas is love, Christ-mas is peace; A
C7 F7 1 2
Ours for the tak-ing just fol-low the mas-ter. cease.
time for hat-ing and fight-ing to
B♭ E♭ B♭
Christ-mas time, mis-tle-toe and wine, child-ren sing-ing
F F7
Chris-ti-an rhyme With logs on the fire and gifts on the
B♭ 1-3 4
tree; A time to re-joice in the good that we see. see.

49

Mony Mony

Words & Music by Bobby Bloom, Ritchie Cordell, Bo Gentry & Tommy James

Moderately
C
F
1. Here she comes now, say, Mo-ny Mo - ny.
2. Wake me, shake me, Mo-ny Mo - ny.
C
Shoot 'em down, turn a - round, come on, Mo - ny.
Shot - gun git it done, come on, Mo - ny.
F
C
Hey, she gives me lov - in', I feel
Don't stop look - in', it feels
all right now.
so good, yeah.
F
C
You've got me
toss - in', turn - in' the mid - dle of the night, and I feel all right. I say Yeah!
Don't stop now. Come on, Mo - ny. Come on, Mo - ny, Yeah!
F
G
(Yeah!) Yeah! (Yeah!) Yeah! (Yeah!) Yeah! (Yeah!) Yeah!

Chorus
C
B♭
C
B♭
C
(Yeah!) Yeah! You make me feel (Mo-ny Mo-ny) so (Mo-ny Mo-ny)
B♭
C
B♭
C
F
E♭
3 fr.
F
good. (Mo-ny Mo-ny) Yeah! (Mo-ny Mo-ny) Yeah! (Mo-ny Mo-ny)
E♭
3 fr.
F
E♭
3 fr.
F
E♭
3 fr.
F
Yeah! (Mo-ny Mo-ny) Yeah! (Mo-ny Mo-ny) Yeah! (Mo-ny Mo-ny) Yeah!
G
(Yeah!) Yeah! (Yeah!) Yeah!
1.
(Yeah!) Yeah! (Yeah!) Yeah! (Yeah!) Yeah! (Yeah!)
(Instrumental)
2.
Repeat ad lib. till fade-out
C
B♭
C
B♭
C

MOON RIVER

Words by Johnny Mercer
Music by Henry Mancini

Moderately slow
C
Am
F
mf
Moon River, wider than a
C
F
C
mile, I'm crossin' you in style some
Bm7(b5)
E7
Am
day, Old dream
C7
F
Bb9(b5)
maker, you heartbreaker, Where-
Am
Am7
F#m7(b5)
B7
Em7
A7
ever you're goin', I'm goin' your
Dm7
G9
fr4
C
Am
way. Two drifters,

F
C
F
Off to see the world, There's such a lot of
C
Bm7(b5)
E7
world to see, We're
Am
Am7
F#m7(b5)
F13
F7
aft - er the same rain - bow's
C
F
C
end, Wait - in' 'round the bend,
F
C
Am
my huck - le - ber - ry friend, Moon
Dm7
G7
G13
fr3
F
Em
Dm7
C
Riv - er and me.

51
MICHELLE

Words & Music by John Lennon & Paul McCartney

Moderately
D Gm7 C B♭7 A B♭7 A
Mi-chelle, ma belle. These are words that go to-geth-er well, my Mi - chelle.
D Gm7 C B♭7 A B♭7
Mi - chelle, ma belle sont les mots qui vont très bien en - semble, très bien en -
A Dm Cm F7
semble. I love you, I love you, I love you, That's all I want to
I need you, I need you, I need you, I need to make you
want you, I want you, I want you, I think you know by
B♭ A Dm Gm Dm D♭+
say. Un-til I find a way I will say the on - ly
see what you mean to me. Un - til I do, I'm
now. I'll get to you some - how. Un - til I do, I'm
Dm7 Dm6 Gm7 To Coda 1 A 2 A D.S. al
words I know that you'll un - der - stand.
hop - ing you will know what I mean. I
tell - ing you so you'll un - der -
CODA
A D Gm7 C B♭7
stand. Mi - chelle, ma belle sont les mots qui vont très bien en -
A B♭7 A Dm Gm Dm Gm
semble, très bien en - semble. I will say the on - ly words I know that
Dm A D Gm7 C7 B♭ A
you'll un - der - stand, my Mi - chelle.

MR. TAMBOURINE MAN

Words & Music by Bob Dylan

Moderate 2
G A D G
Hey! Mis-ter Tam-bou-rine Man, play a song for me, I'm not
D G Em A
sleep-y and there is no place I'm go-in' to.
G A D G
Hey! Mis-ter Tam-bou-rine Man, play a song for me. In the
D G Em A7 D G D
fine
jin-gle jan-gle morn-in' I'll come fol-low-in' you.
Verse
G A D G
Tho' I know that eve-nin's em-pire has re-turned in-to sand,
D G D G Em
Van-ished from my hand, Left me blind-ly here to stand, but still not
A G A
sleep-in'. My wear-i-ness a-maz-es me, I'm
D G D G
brand-ed on my feet. I have no one to meet, And the
D G Em A
an-cient emp-ty street's too dead for dream-in'.

53
MULL OF KINTYRE

Words & Music by Paul McCartney & Denny Laine

Moderately slow
A
D
Mull of Kin - tyre, Oh mist roll - ing in from the
sea, My de - sire is al - ways to be here Oh Mull of Kin-
- tyre.
1
Far have I trav-elled and
much have I seen, Dark dis - tant moun-tains with val - leys of
green. Past paint - ed des- erts, the sun-set's on fire, As he car
- ries me home to the Mull of Kin - tyre.
E
E7

2
A
A7
D
Sweep through the heath-er like deer in the
G
D
glen. Car - ry me back to the days I knew then,
G
Nights when we sang like a heav - en - ly choir of the life and the
A
A7
D
D
times of the Mull of Kin - tyre.
Mull of Kin-
G
D
- tyre Oh mist roll - ing in from the sea, My de - sire is
G
D
1
al - ways to be there Oh Mull of Kin - tyre.
2
D
A
Repeat to fade

MY SWEET LORD

Words & Music by George Harrison

Moderately
B♭
Fm
B♭
My sweet Lord,
mm my Lord,
Fm
B♭
Fm
B♭
mm my Lord,
I real-ly want to
E♭
Cm
E♭
Cm
see you.
know you.
Real-ly want to be with you.
Real-ly want to go with you.
E♭
E°
C7
Real-ly want to see you, Lord, but it takes so long, my Lord,
Real-ly want to show you, Lord, that it won't take long, my Lord,
Fm
B♭
Fm
B♭
My sweet Lord,
My sweet Lord,

Fm
B♭
mm — my — Lord, —
mm — my — Lord,
mm — my — Lord, —
my — sweet — Lord,
Fm
B♭
E♭
I real - ly want to
I real - ly want to see you.
E♭7
Real-ly want to see you.
Real -ly want to
C7
F
see — you Lord, —
Real-ly want to see you Lord, — but it takes
F♯o
D7
Gm
Cm
— so long — my Lord, —
my — sweet Lord,
Gm
C
Gm
C
—
mm — my — Lord, —
Gm
C
D.S. al Fade
my, my, — my Lord, —
my — sweet Lord, —

55
OB-LA-DI, OB-LA-DA

Words & Music by John Lennon & Paul McCartney

Bright tempo
Bb F7
Des-mond has a bar-row in the mar- ket place Mol -
Bb
- ly is the sing-er in a band. Des - mond says to
Eb Bb
Mol - ly, "Girl, I like your face," And Mol - ly says this as she
F7 Bb Bb
takes him by the hand, Ob - la - di ob - la - da, life goes on,
Dm Gm Bb
Bra - la la, How the life goes on.
Dm Gm
Ob -la - di Ob - la da Life goes on, Bra - la
Bb F7 To Coda Bb 1. 2.
la, How the life goes on.

Eb
In a cou-ple of years they have built a home sweet home

Bb
Cm
Bb
Bb9
Eb
With a cou-ple of

Bb
kids run-ning in the yard Of Des-mond and Mol-

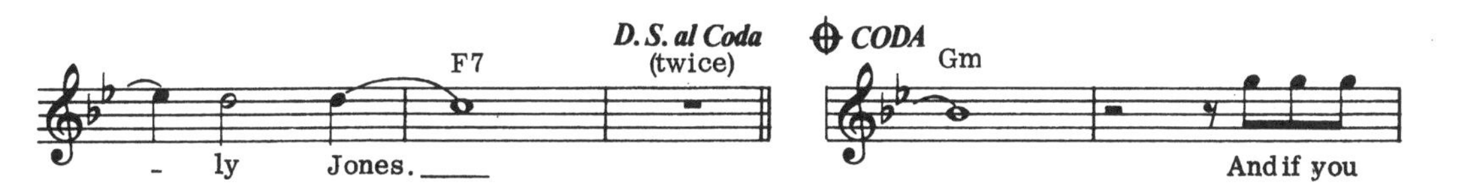
D. S. al Coda
(twice)
CODA
F7
Gm
-ly Jones.
And if you

F7
Bb
want some fun take Ob-la di-bla da.

2. Desmond takes a trolley to the jeweller's stores,
Buys a twenty carat golden ring,
Takes it back to Molly waiting at the door,
And as he gives it to her she begins to sing,

3. Happy ever after in the market place
Desmond let's the children lend a hand;
Molly stays at home and does her pretty face,
And in the evening she still sings it with the hand.

4. Happy ever after in the market place
Molly lets the children lend a hand;
Desmond stays at home and does his pretty face,
And in the evening she's a singer with the band.

56
THE NAME OF THE GAME

Words & Music by Benny Andersson, Björn Ulvaeus & Stig Anderson

F♯m C♯m F♯m C♯m
I've seen you twice __ in a short time __
It seems to me __ For ev - 'ry time __
F♯m C♯m F♯m B
On - ly a week __ since we start - ed __
I'm get - ting more __ o - pen heart - ed. __
F♯m B C♯m Dmaj7
I was an im-pos-sib-le case, No one ev-er could reach __ me.
F♯m B C♯m Dmaj7
But I think I can see in your face there's a lot you can teach __ me,
Bm7 E11 A
__ So I wan-na know, What's the name of the game,
D E E/D A
Does it mean an - y - thing __ to you? __
D E D A
What's the name of the game, __

D E E/D A
Can you feel it the way I do?
C♯ F♯m E/D♯ E
Tell me please 'cause I have to know, I'm a
C♯ F♯m B/D♯ E11
bash-ful child be-gin-ning to grow.
A D
And you make me talk, And you make me feel
A D G D
And you make me show what I'm try-ing to
A D
con-ceal. If I trust in you would you let me down,
A F♯m
Would you laugh at me? If I said I care
G♯m7 C♯7 Dmaj7
for you could you feel the same

Bm7
E11
F♯m
way too? I wan-na know the name of the game.
C♯m
F♯m
C♯m
F♯m
C♯m
F♯m
B
2 Bm7
E11
wan-na know
Em7
E11
Oh yes, I wan-na know: the name of the game.
A
D
E
E/D
Does it mean an-y-thing to you?
A
D
E
D
What's the name of the
A
D
E
E/D
game, Can you feel it the way I do?
A
D
E
D
Repeat to fade
What's the name of the game

57

Oh, Pretty Woman

Words & Music by Roy Orbison & Bill Dees

Moderato
CHORUS
F
Pret-ty wo-man walk-ing

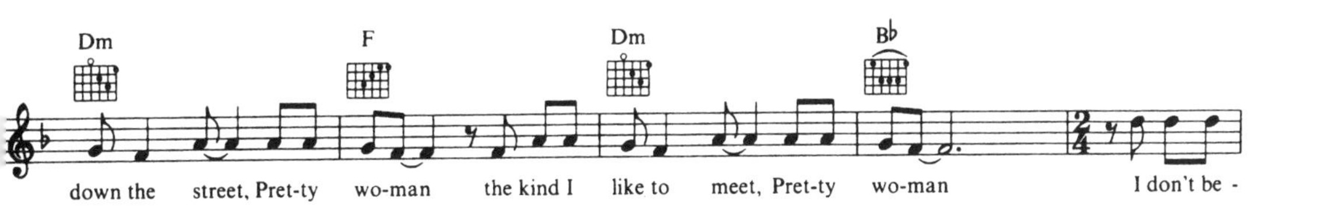
Dm
F
Dm
B♭
down the street, Pret-ty wo-man the kind I like to meet, Pret-ty wo-man I don't be -

C7
- lieve you, you're not the truth No-one could look as good as you
Mer-cy

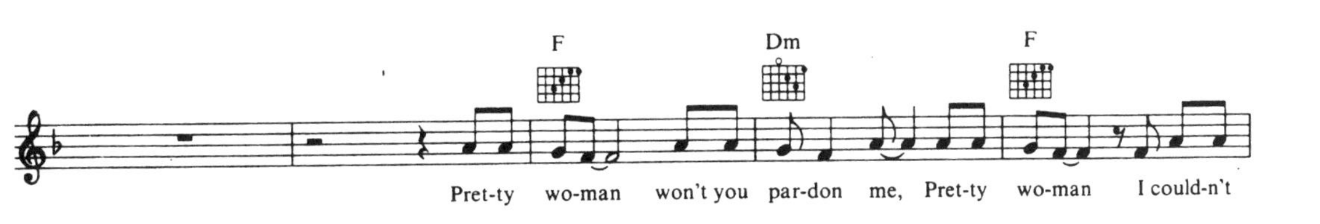
F
Dm
F
Pret-ty wo-man won't you par-don me, Pret-ty wo-man I could-n't

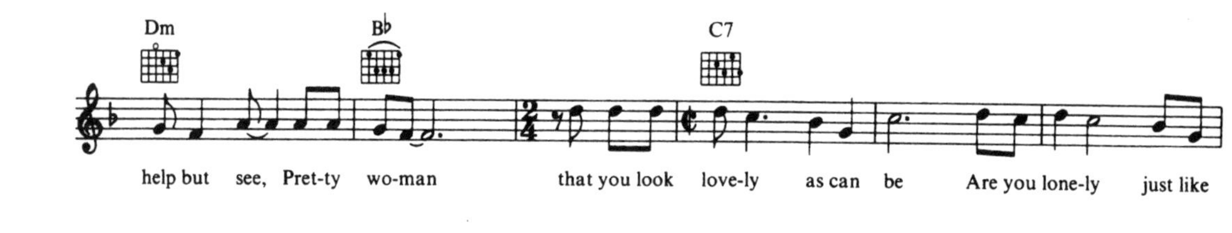
Dm
B♭
C7
help but see, Pret-ty wo-man that you look love-ly as can be Are you lone-ly just like

B♭m
me?
Pret-ty wo-man

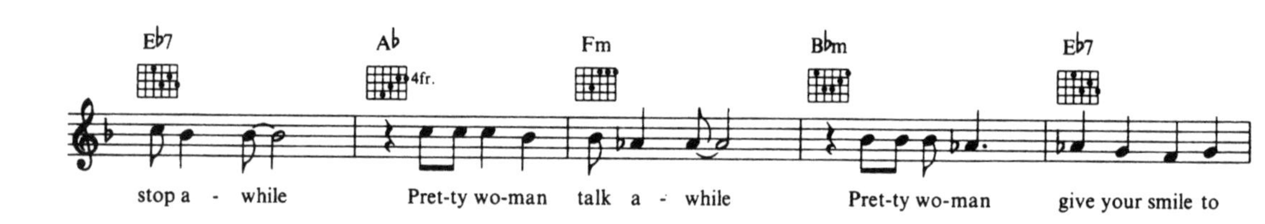
E♭7
A♭
4fr.
Fm
B♭m
E♭7
stop a - while Pret-ty wo-man talk a - while Pret-ty wo-man give your smile to

A♭
4fr.
B♭m
E♭7
A♭
4fr.
Fm
me Pret-ty wo-man yeah, yeah, yeah, Pret-ty wo-man look my way

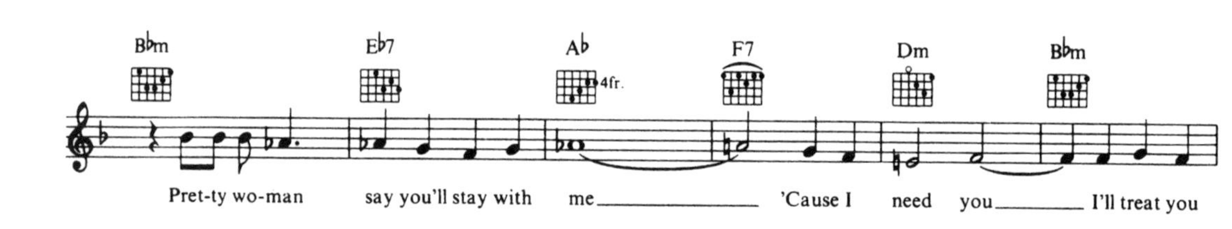
B♭m
E♭7
A♭
4fr.
F7
Dm
B♭m
Pret-ty wo-man say you'll stay with me 'Cause I need you I'll treat you

C7
F
Dm
B♭m
C7
right Come to me ba - by Be mine to - night

F
Dm
F
Dm
Pret-ty wo-man don't walk on by, Pret-ty wo-man don't make me cry, Pret-ty

B♭
C7
wo-man don't walk a - way Hey, O. K. If that's the

way it must be, O. K. I guess I'll go on home it's late There'll be to - mor-row night, but

wait! What do I see Is she walk-ing back to

me? Yeah, she's walk-ing back to me!

1 F
2 F
Oh, Pret-ty wo-man Pret-ty wo-man

58

THE POWER OF LOVE

Words & Music by Candy de Rouge, Gunther Mende, Jennifer Rush & Susan Applegate

Moderato
B♭
Gm
The whis-pers in the morn-ing of lo - vers sleep-ing tight, are roll-ing by like

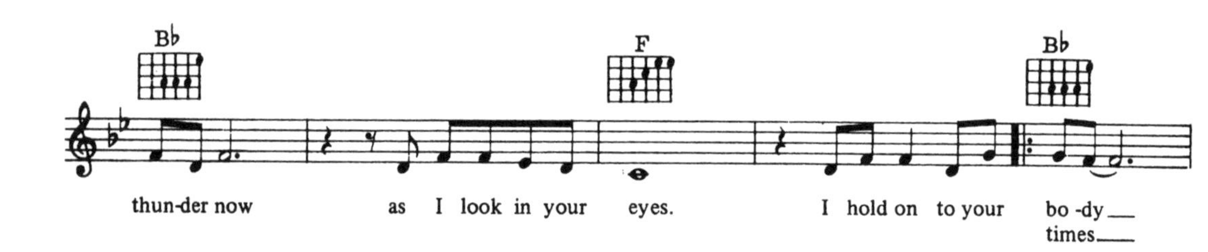
B♭
F
B♭
thun-der now as I look in your eyes. I hold on to your bo -dy
times

Gm
E♭
B♭
and feel each move you make; Your voice is warm and ten-der, A love that I could not for -
it seems I'm far a - way; But ne- ver won-der where I am 'cause I am al -ways by your

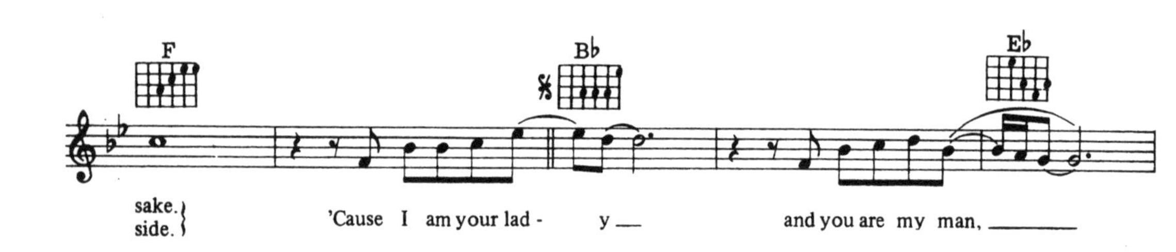
F
B♭
E♭
sake.
side.
'Cause I am your lad - y and you are my man,

Cm
F
1
When ev-er you reach for me I'll do all that I can.
I'm gon-na do
Ev-en though there may be

2
B♭
E♭
We're head-ing for some-thing, some-where I've ne-ver been, Some-times I am fright-

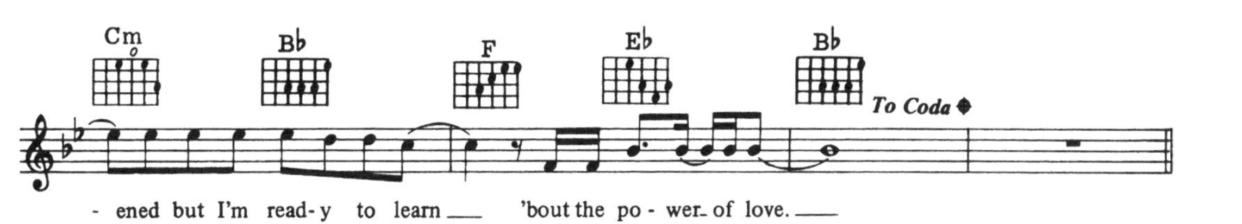
Cm
B♭
F
E♭
B♭
To Coda
- ened but I'm read-y to learn 'bout the po - wer of love.

E♭
F
B♭
E♭
F
Gm
E♭
F
The sound of your heart beat-ing made it clear sud-den-ly. The feel- ing that I

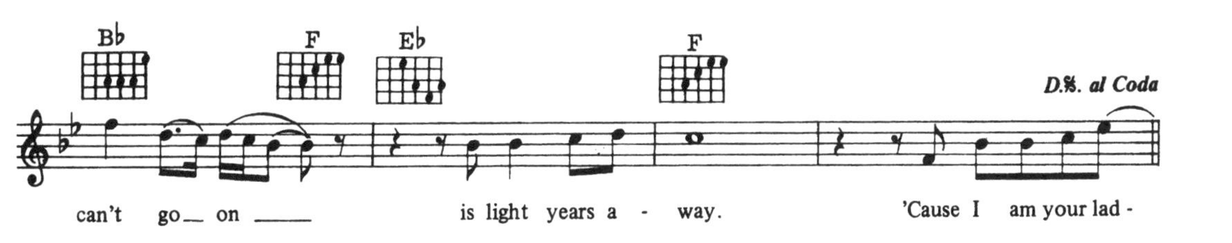
B♭
F
E♭
F
D.𝄋. al Coda
can't go on is light years a - way. 'Cause I am your lad -

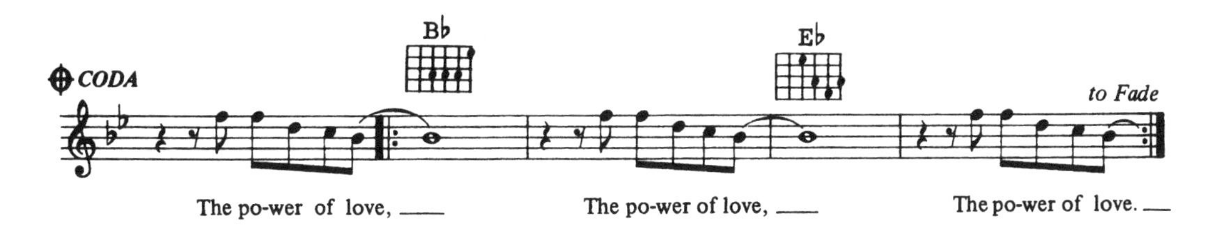
CODA
B♭
E♭
to Fade
The po-wer of love, The po-wer of love, The po-wer of love.

59
ONLY THE LONELY

Words & Music by Roy Orbison & Joe Melson

Moderato
G
Am
On - ly the lone - ly know the way I feel to - night On - ly the
D7
Am7
D7
G
lone - ly know this feel - ing ain't right There goes my
G7
ba - by There goes my heart They've gone for -
C
A7
D7
ev - er So far a - part But on - ly the
G
G7
C
D7
lone - ly know why I cry
1
G
D7
2
G
on - ly the lone - ly on - ly the lone - ly

2. Only the lonely know the heartaches I've been through
Only the lonely know I cry and cry for you
Maybe tomorrow. a new romance
No more sorrow, but that's the chance
You've got to take if you're lonely
Heartbreak, Only the lonely.

RAINDROPS KEEP FALLING ON MY HEAD

Words by Hal David
Music by Burt Bacharach

Rhythmically
F
Fmaj7
F7
1. Rain - drops keep fall-in' on my head, and just like the guy whose feet are
2. did me some talk-in' to the sun, and I said I did-n't like the
D.%. Rain - drops keep fall-in' on my head, but that does-n't mean my eyes will
Eb
Am7
D7
D9
Am7
D7
Gm7
too big for his bed, noth-in' seems to fit. Those rain-drops are fall-in' on my
way he got things done, sleep-in' on the job. Those rain-drops are fall-in' on my
soon be turn- in' red, cry-in's not for me. 'Cause I'm nev-er gon-na stop the
To Coda 3rd time)
Bb/C
C
F
Fmaj7
B7
head, they keep fall-in'. So I just
head, they keep fall-in'! But there's one thing I know, The blues
rain by com-plain-in'. Be-cause I'm
Eb
C
C7
Am7
they send to meet me won't de-feat me. It won't be long till
D.%. al Coda
D9
Gm7
Gm9
Gm7
Bb/C
C
Bb/C
C
hap-pi - ness steps up to greet me.
CODA
F
Fmaj7
Gm7
Eb/C
F
free, noth-in's wor-ry - in' me.

61

THE REFLEX

Words & Music by Simon Le Bon, Andy Taylor, Roger Taylor, John Taylor & Nick Rhodes

Moderato
Gm F Cm Gm
mf
You gone too far this time, but I'm
F C Gm F
danc - ing on the Val - en - tine. I tell you some-bo - dy's
Cm Gm F C Gm
fool-ing a - round with my chanc - es on the dan - ger line. I'll
Gm F Cm Gm
cross that bridge when I find it, an- oth- er day to
I'm on a ride and I want to get off, but they
F C Gm F
make my stand, Oh. High time is no time for de-
won't slow down the round- a - bout. I sold the Re - noir and the
Cm Gm F C Gm
cid - ing if I should find a help-ing hand, Oh.
T. V. set, don't wan-na be a - round when this gets out. So
Am F Am F
why don't you use it, Try not to bruise it,

Am F C F Am
buy time don't lose it. Why don't you
F Am F Am
use it. Try not to bruise it. Buy time don't
F G CHORUS D
lose it. The Re - flex is an on-
The Re - flex,
C G
ly child. He's wait - ing by the park. The
what a game, He's hid - ing all the cards.
D C
Re - flex is in charge of find - ing trea-sure in the dark.
F D
And watch-ing ov - er luck - y clo - ver.
C G D
Is - n't that bi - zarre, Ev - 'ry lit-tle thing The Re-
C F Gm F
flex does leaves you answered with a ques-tion mark. (instrumental)
Cm Gm F 1 Cm Gm 2 Cm Gm D. S.
(To FADE on Chorus)

62

RIVERS OF BABYLON

Words & Music by Frank Farian, George Reyam, Brent Dowe & James McNaughton

G
By the riv-ers of Ba-by-lon there we sat down,
D
G
Yeah we wept when we re-mem-bered Zi - on.
1
2
G
By the riv-ers of For there, they that car-ried us a-way in cap-tiv- i - ty, re-
C
G
-quir-ing of us a song. Now how shall we sing the Lord's song in a
D
G
1
2
G
strange land? For there, they that ah
G
ah

D
To Coda
G
Let the
G D G D
words of our mouths and the med-i-ta-tions of our hearts be ac-
G D7 G
1
-cept-a-ble in thy sight here to-night. Let the
2 G G
By the riv-ers of Ba-by-lon, there we sat down, Yeah we
D7 G
1 2 D.S. al Coda
wept when we re-mem-bered Zi-on. By the riv-ers of Ah
CODA G G
-(ah) By the riv-ers of Ba-by-lon
D7
there we sat down, Yeah we wept
G
Repeat to fade
when we re-mem-bered Zi-on. By the riv-ers of

63

A Rockin' Good Way (To Mess Around And Fall In Love)

Words & Music by Brook Benton, Luchi de Jesus & Clyde Otis

Moderately
F
If you're gon-na give me good kiss-es like that, Hon-ey don't you know I'm gon-na
F7
Bb9
give 'em right back, 'cos that's a kiss- in' good way, That's a
F
C7
kiss- in' good way, That's a kiss-in' good way to
Bb9
F
F7
mess a- round and fall in love. If you're gon- na start out,
Hug-gin' me tight, Don't mess a - round, just hug me right, 'cos that's a
Bb9
F
hug-gin' good way, That's a hug-gin' good way, That's a

C7
Bb9
F
hug-gin' good way to mess a-round and fall in love.
You know you
Bb
Bb9
F
called me on the phone,
And just be-cause I was a-lone,
Bb
Bb9
G7
Yes, you came a-round a-woo-ing,
You bet-ter ask some-bo-dy if you
C7
F
don't know what you're do-ing.
Now that you've kissed me and rocked my soul,
F7
Bb9
Don't come a-round knock-in' rock and roll,
'cos that's A Rock-in' Good Way,
F
C7
That's A Rock-in' Good Way,
That's A Rock-in' Good Way to
Bb9
1 F
2 F
mess a-round and fall in love.

64
RELEASE ME

Words & Music by Eddie Miller, Dub Williams & Robert Yount

Moderato

F Fdim Gm7 F D7 Gm7 C7
1. Please re - lease me, let me go, For I don't
2. I have found a new love dear, And I will

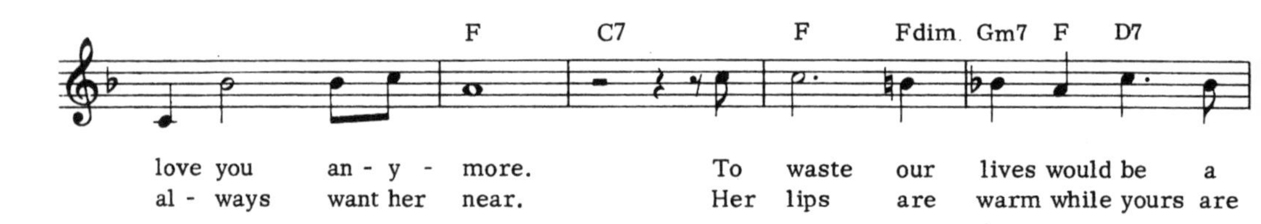
F C7 F Fdim Gm7 F D7
love you an - y - more. To waste our lives would be a
al - ways want her near. Her lips are warm while yours are

Gm7 F C7 F C7
sin. Re - lease me and let me love a - gain.
cold. Re - lease me, my dar-ling, let me go.

F Fdim Gm7 F D7 Gm7 C7
3. Please re - lease me, can't you see You'd be a

F C7 F Fdim Gm7 F D7
fool to cling to me? To live a lie would bring us

Gm7 F C7 F Bb F
pain, So re -lease me and let me love a - gain.

SAILING

Words & Music by Gavin Sutherland

Moderato
B♭ Gm E♭ B♭
p
I am sail-ing, I am sail-ing home a-gain 'cross the sea. I am
fly-ing, I am fly-ing like a bird 'cross the sea. I am
C7 Gm Cm7 1 B♭ F7
sail-ing stor-my wa-ters, to be near you, to be free. I am
fly-ing, pass-ing high clouds to be near you, to be
2 B♭ F7 B♭ Gm E♭ B♭
mf
free. Can you hear me, can you hear me thro' the dark night, far a-way? I am
C7 Gm Cm7 B♭ F7
f
dy-ing, for ev-er try-ing to be with you; who can say? Can you
B♭ Gm E♭ B♭
hear me, can you hear me thro' the dark night, far a-way. I am
sail-ing, we are sail-ing home a-gain 'cross the sea. We are
C7 Gm Cm7 1 B♭ F7
dy-ing, for ev-er try-ing to be with you; who can say?
sail-ing stor-my wa-ters, to be near you, to be
Repeat and fade
2 B♭ G7 Cm B♭ G7
We are free. Oh Lord to be near you, to be free. Oh Lord to be

66

SHE LOVES YOU

Words & Music by John Lennon & Paul McCartney

Moderately
Cm
F7
She loves you yeh, yeh, yeh, She loves you yeh,
Ab
Eb
Db
yeh, yeh, She loves you yeh, yeh, yeh, yeh! 1. You
Eb
Cm
Gm
think you've lost your love, Well, I saw her yes - ter -
said you hurt her so, She al - most lost her
know it's up to you, I think it's on - ly
Bb7
Eb
Cm
-day-yi - yay. It's you she's think - ing of, And she
mind. And now she says she knows You're
fair, Pride can hurt you too, A -
Gm
Eb
told me what to say-yi- yay. She says she
not the hurt - ing kind. She says she
-pol - a - gize to her. Be-cause she
loves you, and you

Cm
know that can't be bad, Yes, she
Abm
Eb7
1 Db Bb7
loves you, and you know you should be glad. 2. She
2 Bb
Cm
F
Oo She loves you yeh, yeh, yeh, She loves you, yeh,
F7
Abm
Bb7+
Bb7
Eb
To Coda
yeh, yeh, And with a love like that you know you should be glad.
D.%. al Coda
3. You
CODA
Cm
Abm
With a love like that you
Bb7+
Bb7
Eb
Cm
know you should be glad, Yeh,
rit.
a tempo
Ab
Eb6
yeh, yeh, yeh, yeh, yeh, yeh.

67

SOMETHIN' STUPID

Words & Music by C. Carson Parks

Moderately slow
F
I know I stand in line un-til you think you have the time to spend an
prac-tice ev-'ry day to find some cle-ver lines to say to make the

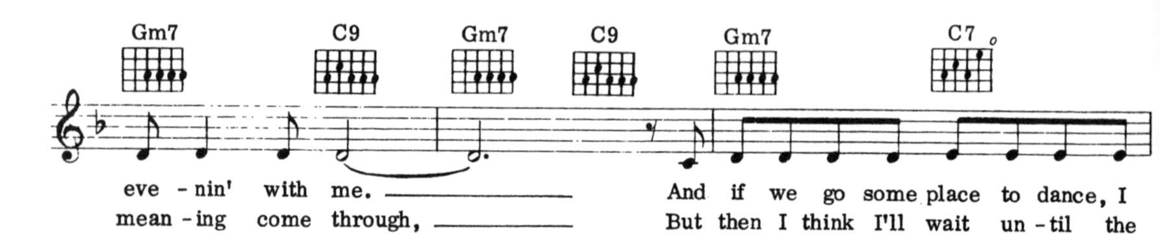
Gm7 C9 Gm7 C9 Gm7 C7
eve-nin' with me. And if we go some place to dance, I
mean-ing come through, But then I think I'll wait un-til the

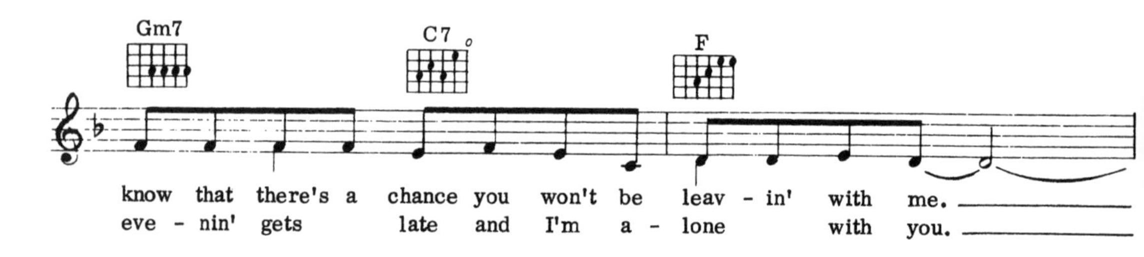
Gm7 C7 F
know that there's a chance you won't be leav-in' with me.
eve-nin' gets late and I'm a-lone with you.

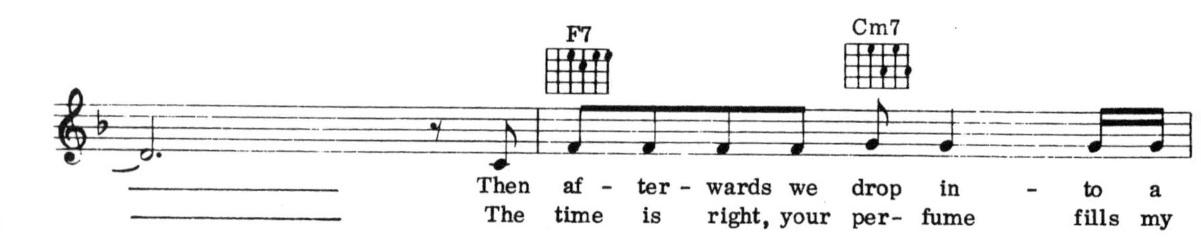
F7 Cm7
Then af-ter-wards we drop in-to a
The time is right, your per-fume fills my

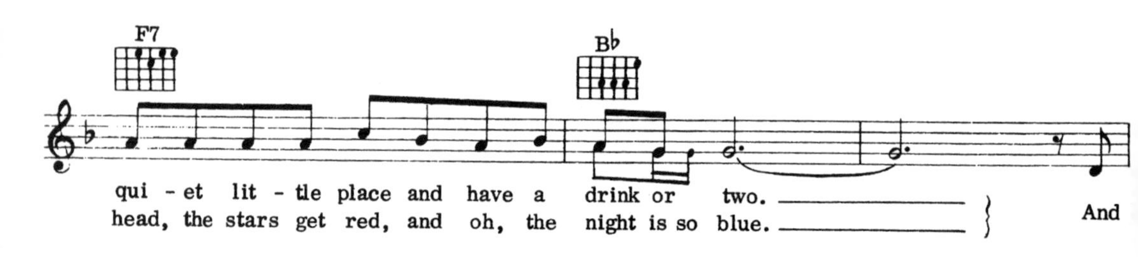
F7 Bb
qui-et lit-tle place and have a drink or two.
head, the stars get red, and oh, the night is so blue.
And

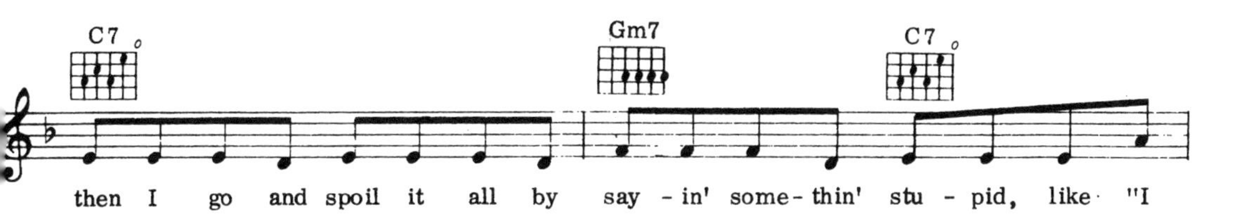
C7
Gm7
C7
then I go and spoil it all by say - in' some- thin' stu - pid, like "I

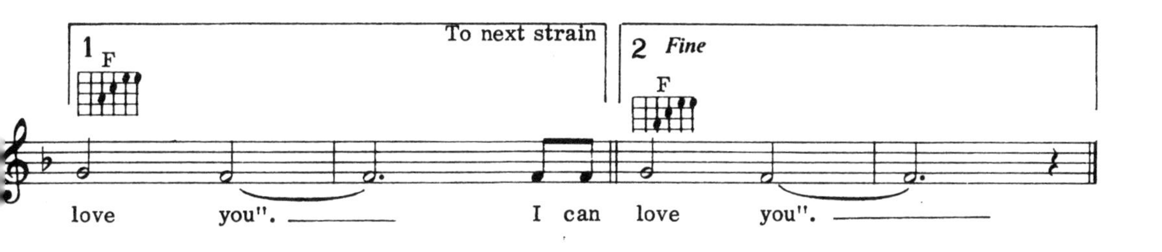
1 F
To next strain
2 Fine
F
love you". I can love you".

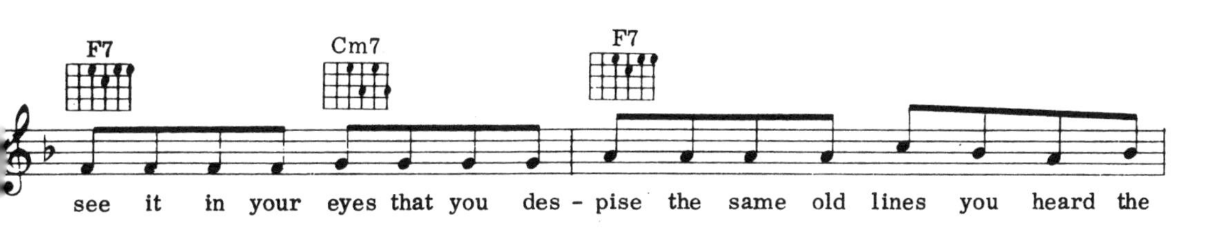
F7
Cm7
F7
see it in your eyes that you des - pise the same old lines you heard the

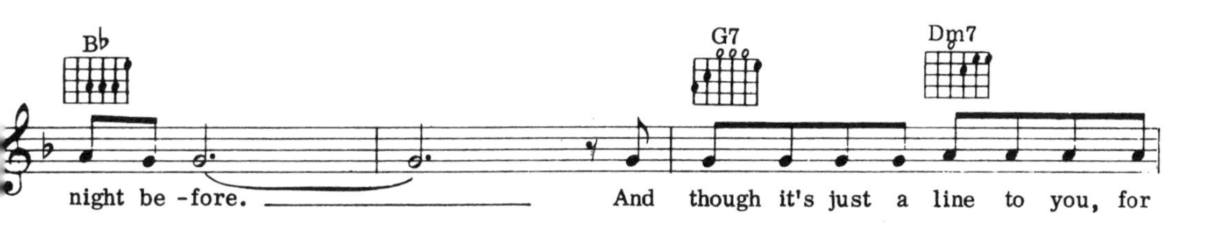
B♭
G7
Dm7
night be -fore. And though it's just a line to you, for

G7
C7
D.C. al Fine
me it's true and nev -er seemed so right be -fore. I

68
SPIRIT IN THE SKY

Words & Music by Norman Greenbaum

Moderato
G
When I die and they lay me to rest,
gon-na go to the place
C
that's the best,
when I lay me down
G
to die
go-in' up
D
to the Spir-it in the sky.
G
Go-in' up to the Spir-it in the sky,
that's where I'm gon-na go
C
when I die,
when I die and they
G
lay me to rest, gon-na go
D
to the place that's the
G
best.
C
Bb
G
Bb
C
G
C
Bb
G
Bb
C

G
Pre-pare your-self, you know it's a must, got-ta have a friend in
Nev-er been a sin-ner I nev-er sinned, I got a friend in
C
Je-sus, So you know that when you die he's
Je-sus, So you know that when I die he's
G
D
gon-na rec-om-mend you to the Spi-rit in the sky. gon-na rec-om-mend you to the
gon-na set me up with the Spi-rit in the sky. oh, set me up with the
G
3
Spi-rit in the sky, that's where you're gon-na go when you die,
Spi-rit in the sky, that's where I'm gon-na go when I die,
C
when you die and they lay you to rest you're gon-na go to the place that's the
when you die and they lay me to rest I'm gon-na go to the place that's the
G
D
1
2
best. best. Go to the place that's the best.
D7
Bb
Keep repeating and fade out

69

STRANGERS IN THE NIGHT

Words by Charles Singleton & Eddie Snyder
Music by Bert Kaempfert

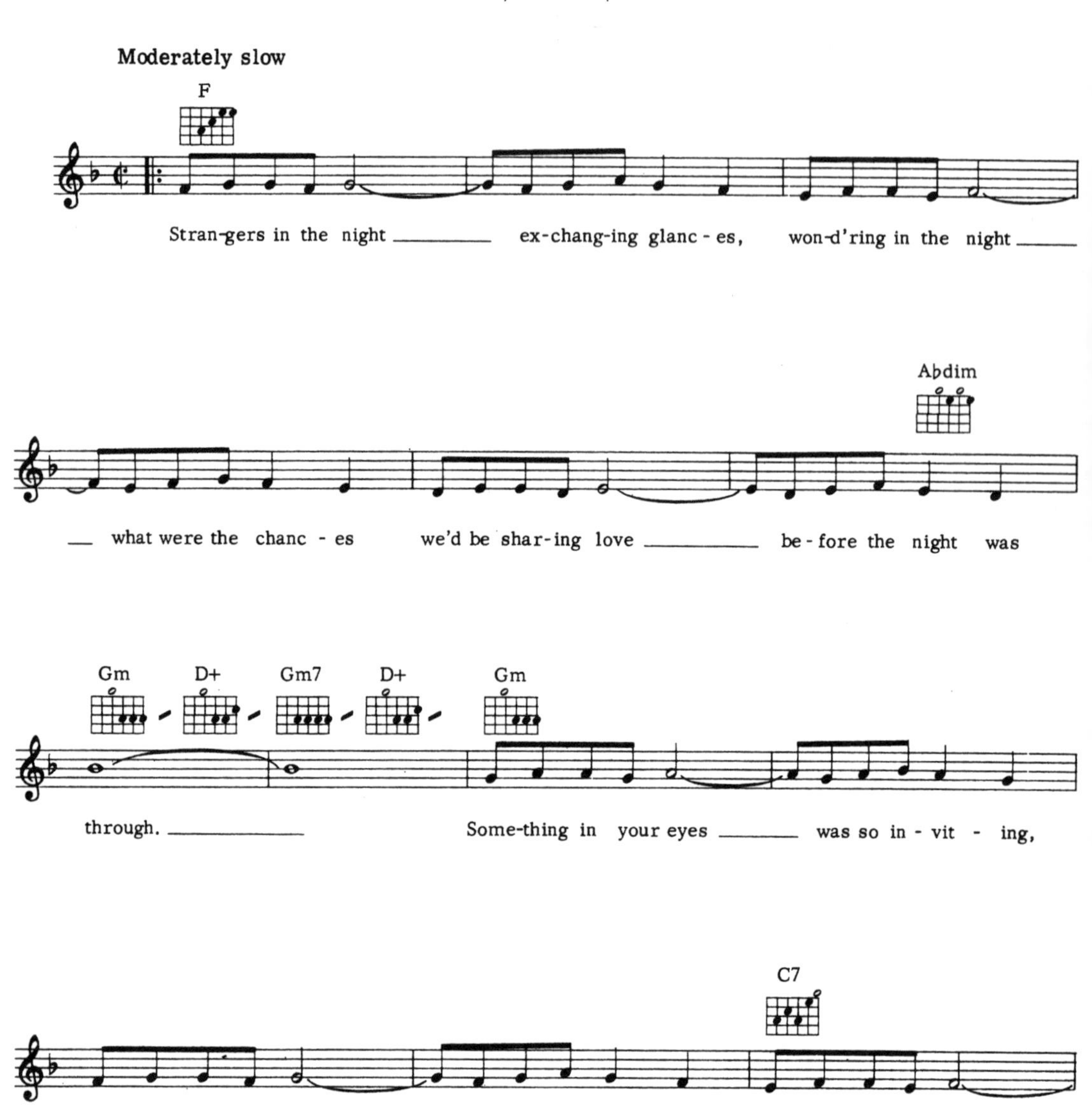
Moderately slow
F
Stran-gers in the night ___ ex-chang-ing glanc - es, won-d'ring in the night ___
Abdim
___ what were the chanc - es we'd be shar-ing love ___ be - fore the night was
Gm
D+
Gm7
D+
Gm
through. ___ Some-thing in your eyes ___ was so in - vit - ing,
C7
some-thing in your smile ___ was so ex - cit - ing, some-thing in my heart ___

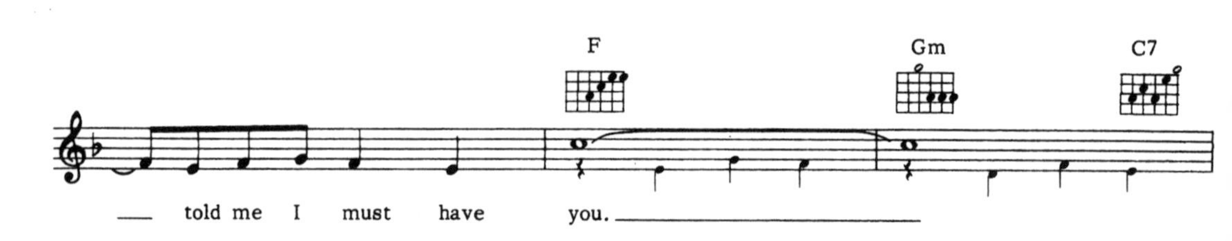
F
Gm
C7
___ told me I must have you. ___

Cm
D7♭9
Stran-gers in the night, two lone-ly peo-ple we were stran-gers in the night
Gm
B♭m
up to the mo-ment when we said our first hel - lo. Lit-tle did we know
F
Dm7
Gm
C7
F
love was just a glance a - way, a warm em-brac-ing dance a - way, and ev-er since that night
we've been to - geth - er, lov-ers at first sight in love for - ev - er.
C7
Gm7
C7
1
F
It turned out so right for stran-gers in the night.
C7
2
F
ritard.
D♭
E♭
F
night.

SUPER TROUPER

Words & Music by Benny Andersson & Björn Ulvaeus

Moderate beat
C
Csus4
C
Csus4
C
Su - per Trou - per beams are gon - na blind _ me but I won't feel
G
Dm
G
blue like I al - ways do. ___ 'Cause some-where in the crowd there's
C
Am
Instrumental
you.
Dm
G
C
Em
Dm
G6
G
I was sick and tired of ev - ery - thing when I called _ you last night from Glas - gow.
Fac-ing twen-ty thou-sand of your friends, how can an - y - one be so lone - ly?
C
Em
Dm
G6
G
All I do is eat and sleep and sing, wish-ing ev - ery show was the last ___ show.
Part of a suc-cess that nev-er ends, still I'm think - ing a - bout you on - ly.
F
C/E
F
C/E
So i - ma-gine I was glad to hear you're com-ing, _ sud-den-ly I feel al - right,
There are mo-ments when I think I'm go-ing cra-zy, ___ but it's gon-na be al - right,

F
C
G sus4
G
and it's gon-na be so dif-ferent when I'm on the stage to - night.
ev-ery-thing will be so dif-ferent when I'm on the stage to - night.
To-night the
C
Csus4
C
Csus4
C
G
Su - per Trou - per lights are gon-na find _ me, shin - ing like the sun,
Dm
G
C
smil - ing, hav - ing fun, feel-ing like a num - ber one. To - night the
C
Csus4
C
Csus4
C
G
Su - per Trou - per beams are gon-na blind _ me, but I won't feel blue
Dm
G
1
2
like I al - ways do 'Cause some-where in the crowd there's
some-where in the crowd there's
C
F
Am
you. So I'll be there when you ar - rive, the sight of
Dm
G
C
G
F
you will prove to me I'm still a - live and when you take me in your arms and hold me
Dm
A7
Dm
G
D.S. and fade
tight I know it's gon - na mean so much to - night. To-night the

Sweets For My Sweet

Words & Music by Doc Pomus & Mort Shuman

Moderately
VERSE
C
F
G
1. If you want - ed that star that shines so bright-ly,
want - ed a dream to keep you smil - ing,
want - ed a love to last for - ev - er, Dar-lin'
To match the star-dust in your eyes, Dar - ling
I'd tell the sand- man you were blue, And I'd
I would send my love your way, And my
I would chase that bright star night-ly,
ask him to keep that sand a pil - in', Un-til your dreams would come
love would not on - ly last for ev- er, But for- ev - er and a
And try to steal it from the
sky.
true.
day.
CHORUS
And I would bring sweets for my sweet, Su-gar for my hon - ey,

C F G F C F
Your thirst-y kiss thrills me so.
Sweets for my sweet,
G F C F G F
Sug - ar for my hon - ey, I'll nev- er ev - er let you go.
1.2.
C F G F
C F G F
3.
C F
2. If you
3. And if you
G F C F C

SOMETHING'S GOTTEN HOLD OF MY HEART

Words & Music by Roger Cook & Roger Greenaway

Gm
F
1. Some-thing's got - ten hold of my heart, keep-ing my soul
2. Some-thing's got - ten hold of my hand, drag-ging my soul
Eb D7 Gm
and my sens- es a - part. Some-thing's got-ten in-to my life,
to a beau- ti - ful land. Yeh Some-thing's has in-vad-ed my night
F Eb D7 Gm F
cut-ting its way through my dreams like a knife, Turn-ing me up
paint- ing my sleep with a co - lour so bright, Chang-ing the grey
Eb D7 Gm F Eb D7
3
turn-ing me down, Mak-ing me smile and mak- ing me
chang-ing the blue, Scar-let for me and scar- let for
1 Gm F
3
frown. In a world that was small I once lived in a time
Bb Eb D7 Gm
3
that was peace and no trou-bles at all. But then you came my

F
Gm
F
way
and a feel - ing un - known shook my heart, made me
C7
F
C7
F
C7
want you to stay,
All of my nights
and
all of my days.
E♭
D7
2
G
Yeh I got-ta tell you now
you.
C
3
3
3
G
Em
A
A7
I've got to know if this is the real
thing.

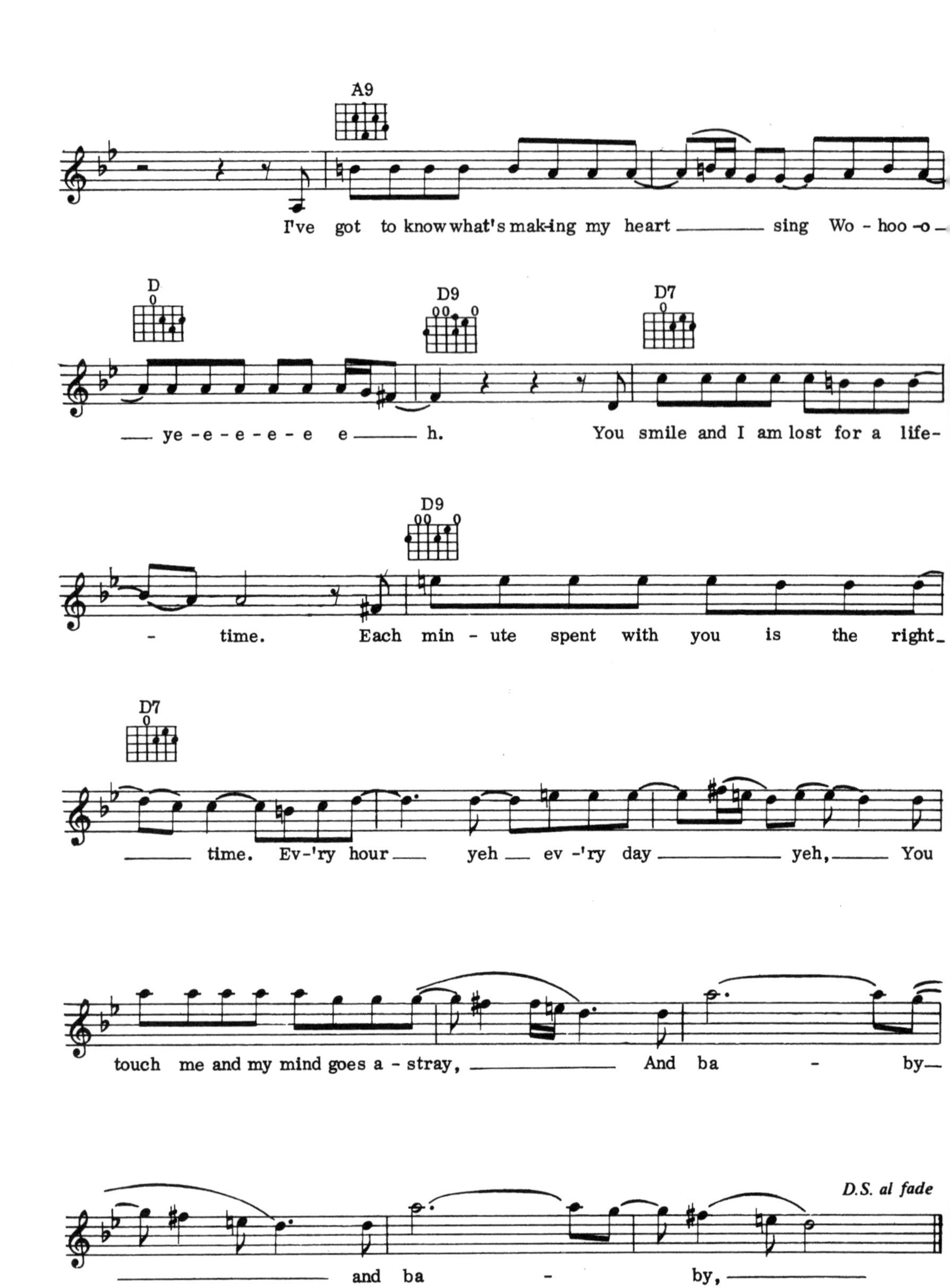
A9
I've got to know what's mak-ing my heart sing Wo - hoo -o-
D
D9
D7
ye - e - e - e - e e h.
You smile and I am lost for a life-
D9
time.
Each min - ute spent with you is the right-
D7
time. Ev-'ry hour yeh ev -'ry day yeh, You
touch me and my mind goes a - stray, And ba - by
and ba - by,
D.S. al fade

73

Take My Breath Away

Words by Tom Whitlock
Music by Giorgio Moroder

Moderately
G
Bm/F♯
Em
mf 1. Watch - ing ev - ery mo - tion in my fool - ish lov - er's game;
(Verses 2 & 3 see block lyric)
Bm/F♯
G
Bm/F♯
On this end - less o - cean, fi - n'lly lov - ers know no shame.
Em
Bm/F♯
Am
Turn - ing and re - turn - ing to
C/G
D
some se - cret place in - side;
G
Bm/F♯
C
watch - ing in slow mo - tion as you turn a - round and say,
D
G
Bm/F♯
To Coda ⊕
"Take my breath a - way."

1.
C
D
G
"Take my breath a - way."
Bm/F♯
C
D
2.
Em
Bm/F♯
G
A
Through the hour - glass I saw
D/F♯
C
G
you, In time you slipped a - way.
A
D/F♯
C
When the mir - ror crashed, I called you and turned to hear you
G
A
say, "If on - ly for to - day I am un - a -

Verse 2:
Watching, I keep waiting, still anticipating love,
Never hesitating to become the fated ones.
Turning and returning to some secret place to hide;
Watching in slow motion as you turn to me and say,
"Take my breath away."

Verse 3:
Watching every motion in this foolish lover's game;
Haunted by the notion somewhere there's a love in flames.
Turning and returning to some secret place inside;
Watching in slow motion as you turn my way and say,
"Take my breath away."

74 TELSTAR

By Joe Meek

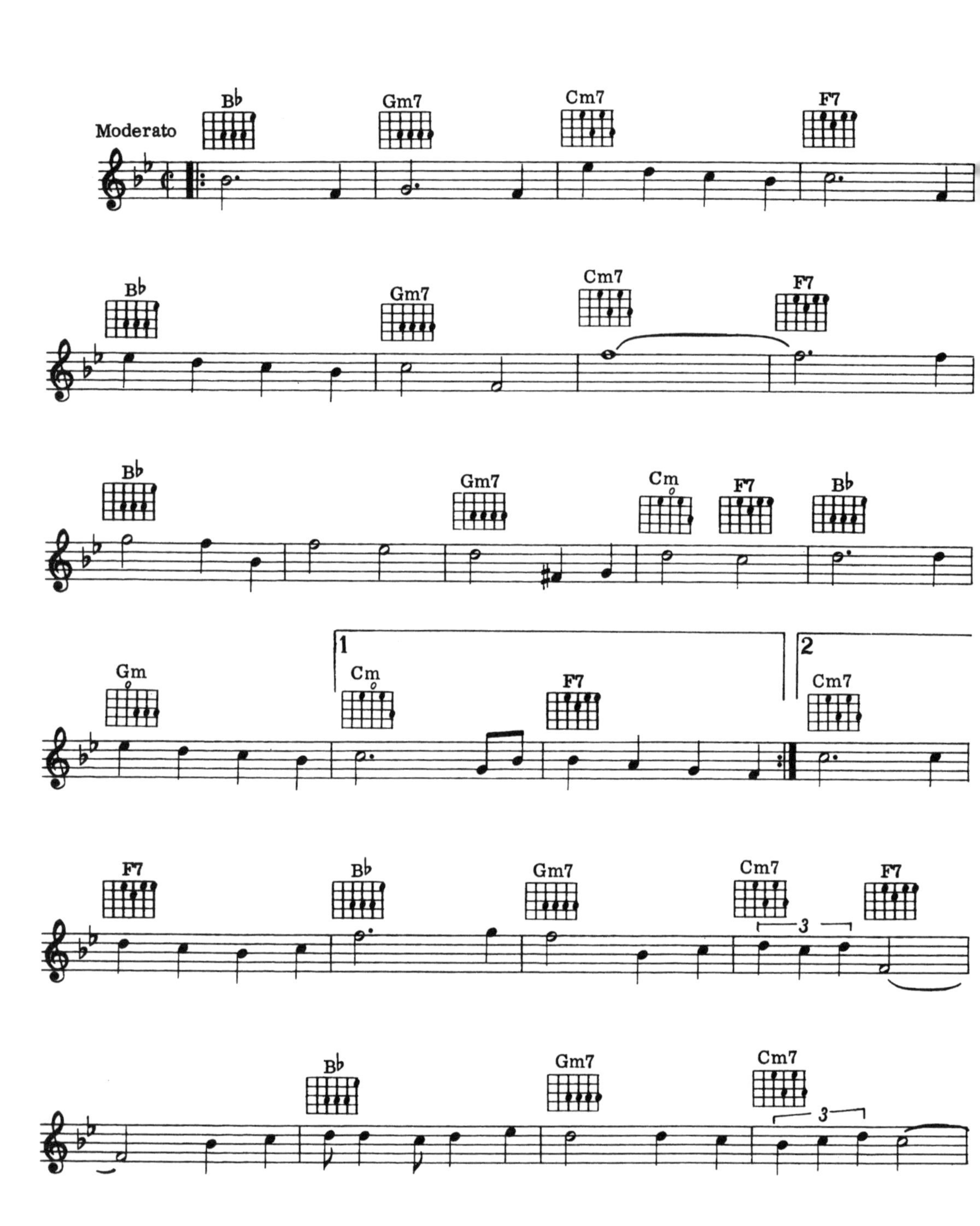

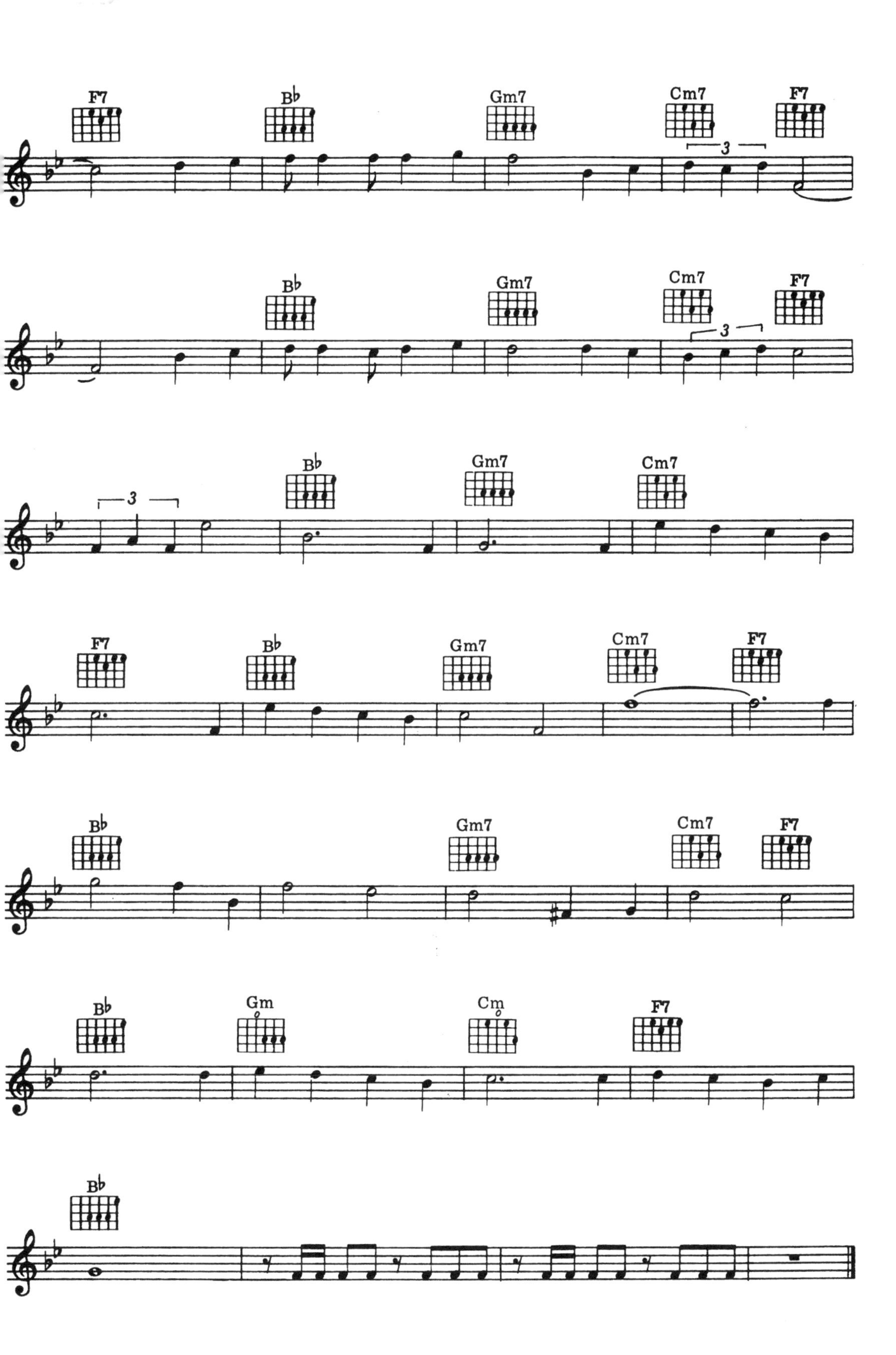
F7
B♭
Gm7
Cm7
F7
3
B♭
Gm7
Cm7
F7
3
3
B♭
Gm7
Cm7
F7
B♭
Gm7
Cm7
F7
B♭
Gm7
Cm7
F7
B♭
Gm
Cm
F7
B♭

75

This Ole House

Words & Music by Stuart Hamblen

Moderately
VERSE
E♭
E♭7
This ole house once knew his child - ren; this ole
house is a - get - tin' sha - ky; this ole
house is a - fraid of thun - der; this ole
A♭
B♭7
house once knew his wife. This ole house was home and
house is a - get - tin' old, This ole house lets in the
house is a - fraid of storms. This ole house just groans and
E♭
A♭
E♭
com - fort as they fought the storms of life. This ole
rain, this ole house lets in the cold. Oh his
trem - bles when the night wind flings its arms. This ole
A♭
house once rang with laugh - ter; this ole house heard man - y
knees are a - get - tin' chil - ly, but he feels no fear nor
house is a - get - tin' fee - ble; this ole house is a - need - in'
B♭7
shouts, Now he trem - bles in the dark - ness when the
pain, 'Cause he seeks a new to - mor - row through a
paint, Just like him it's tuck - ered out, He's a- get - tin'

Eb
CHORUS
Ab
light - nin' walks a - bout.
gold - en win - dow pain.
read - y to meet his fate.
Ain't a - gon-na need this house no
Eb
long - er; ain't a - gon- na need this house no more. Ain't got
Bb7
Eb
time to fix the shing - les: ain't got time to fix the
Ab
floor. Ain't got time to oil the hing - es nor to
Eb
Bb7
mend no win - dow panes. Ain't gon-na need this house no
1.2.
Eb
3.
Eb
long - er; He's a - get - tin' read-y to meet his fate. This ole fate.

76

THAT'LL BE THE DAY

Words & Music by Norman Petty, Buddy Holly & Jerry Allison

Moderately, with a beat
VERSE
E♭
B♭
1. Well, you give me all your lov-in' and your tur - tle dov-in', All ___ your hugs an' kiss-es an' your mon-ey too; ___ Well, you know you love me ba-by,
When Cu-pid shot his dart, He shot it at your heart, ___ So if we ev-er part and I leave you, You say you told me an' you
F7
B♭7
Un-til you tell me, may-be, that some day, well, I'll be through!
told me bold-ly,
C7
CHORUS
Well, ___ That-'ll be the day, when you say good-bye, Yes ___ that-'ll be the day, when you make me cry, Ah, you say you're gon-na leave, you know it's a lie, ___ 'cause That-'ll be the day ___ when I die, Well, ___ when I die. ___
1
2

77

THE TIDE IS HIGH

Words & Music by John Holt, Howard Barrett & Tyrone

Moderately
C F G7 C
mf (Instrumental)
Dm G7 C F6 G7
C F G7 C
The tide is high but I'm
F G C F G
hold - in' on, I'm gon - na be your num - ber one.
C F G C
I'm not the kind - a girl who gives up just like that Oh,
F G C F G
no, It's not the things you do that tease and hurt me bad,

C F G C
But it's the way you do the things you do to me. I'm not the kind-a girl
F G C F G
who gives up just like that, Oh, no. The
C F G C
tide is high but I'm hold - in' on, I'm gon - na be your
F G F G7
num - ber one. Num - ber one.
C F G
Ev - 'ry girl wants you to be her man,
C F G
But I'll wait, my dear, till it's my turn.
C F G
I'm not the kind - a girl who gives up just like

C
F
G
that,
Oh,
no.
The
C
F
G
C
tide is high but I'm hold - in' on,
I'm gon - na be your
F
G
F
G7
F
G7
To Coda
num - ber one.
Num - ber one,
num - ber one.
C
F
G7
C
Dm
G7
(Instrumental)
D.S. al Coda
C
F6
G7
C
F
G7
Coda
C
The tide is high but I'm
F
G
C
F
G7
Repeat to fade
hold - in' on,
I'm gon - na be your num - ber one.
The

Tie A Yellow Ribbon 'Round The Old Oak Tree

Words & Music by Irwin Levine & L. Russell Brown

Fairly bright
F
Am
I'm com-ing home I've done my time
Now I've
Bus dri - ver please look for me
'Cause I
Cm
D7
Gm
got to know what is and is - n't mine
if
could-n't bear to see what I might see
I'm
B♭m
F
Dm
you re -ceived my let - ter tell - in' you I'd soon be free
real - ly still in pris- on and my love she holds the key
A
G7
B♭m
C7
Then you'll know just what to do if you still want me
sim - ple yel - low rib - bon's what I need to set me free
I
B♭m
C7
If you still want me
wrote and told her please
Well
F
Am
tie a yel - low rib - bon 'round the ole oak tree It's been
Cm
D7
Gm
three long years do ya still want me? If

Bbm F A7 Dm
I don't see a rib - bon 'round the ole oak tree I'll
F F+ Dm D7
stay on the bus, For - get a - bout us, put the blame on me. If
Gm Bbm Gm (+5) C7
To Coda
I don't see a yel - low rib - bon round the ole oak
hun - dred yel - low rib - bons 'round the ole the ole oak
F Am Gm7 C7
1
tree.
F Am
2
tree
Cm D7 Gm
RUBATO
Now the
Gm7-5 (Bbm6) F D7
D. S. al Coda
(a tempo)
whole damn bus is cheer - ing and I can't be - lieve I see a
CODA
F Am Gm7 C7 F
Fine
tree

79
THOSE WERE THE DAYS

Words & Music by Gene Raskin

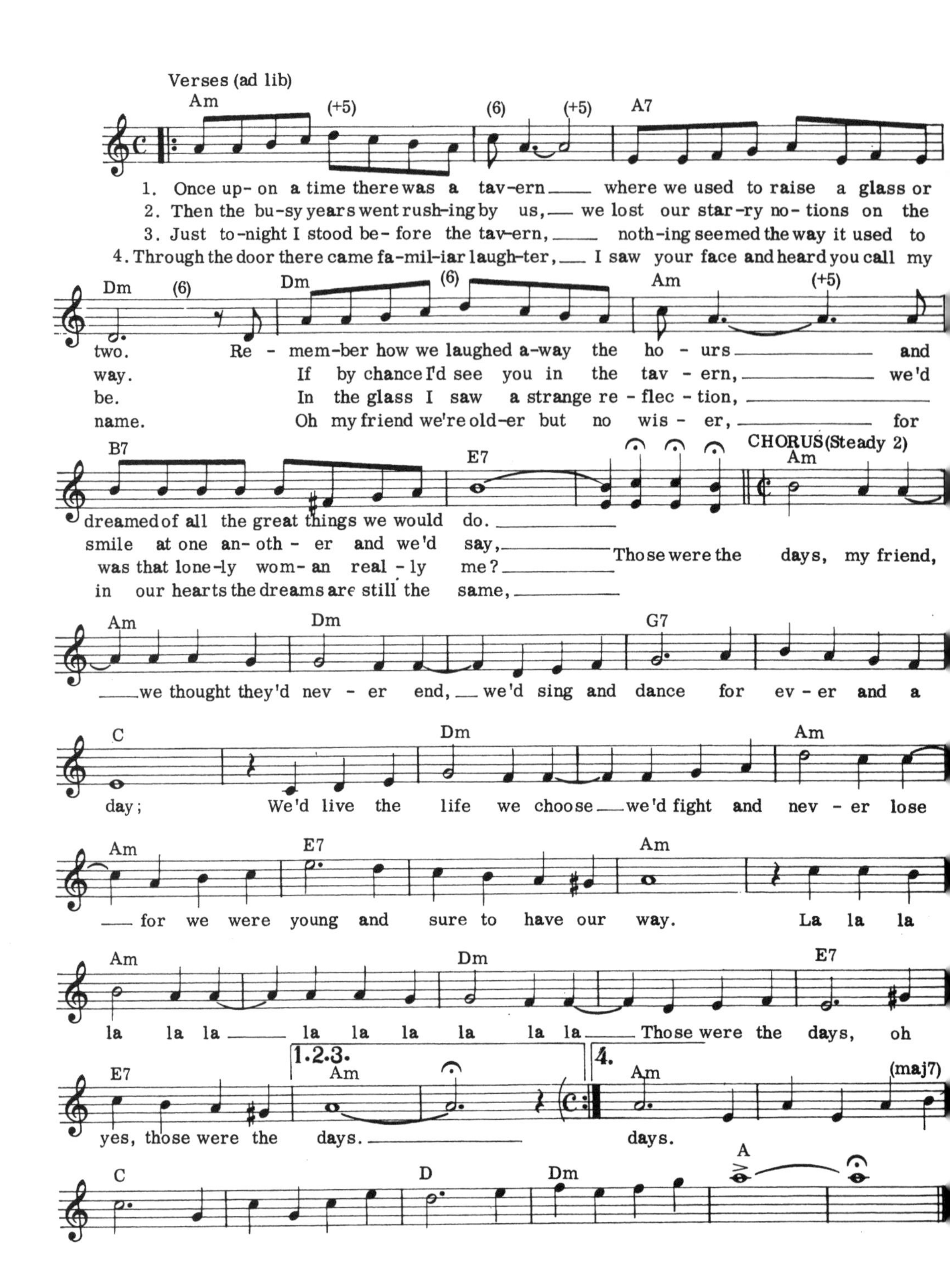
Verses (ad lib)
Am
(+5)
(6)
(+5)
A7
1. Once up- on a time there was a tav-ern where we used to raise a glass or
2. Then the bu-sy years went rush-ing by us, we lost our star-ry no- tions on the
3. Just to-night I stood be- fore the tav-ern, noth-ing seemed the way it used to
4. Through the door there came fa-mil-iar laugh-ter, I saw your face and heard you call my
Dm
(6)
Dm
(6)
Am
(+5)
two. Re - mem-ber how we laughed a-way the ho - urs and
way. If by chance I'd see you in the tav - ern, we'd
be. In the glass I saw a strange re - flec - tion,
name. Oh my friend we're old-er but no wis - er, for
B7
E7
CHORUS (Steady 2)
Am
dreamed of all the great things we would do.
smile at one an- oth - er and we'd say,
was that lone-ly wom- an real - ly me?
in our hearts the dreams are still the same,
Those were the days, my friend,
Am
Dm
G7
we thought they'd nev - er end, we'd sing and dance for ev - er and a
C
Dm
Am
day; We'd live the life we choose we'd fight and nev - er lose
Am
E7
Am
for we were young and sure to have our way. La la la
Am
Dm
E7
la la la la la la la la la Those were the days, oh
E7
1.2.3.
Am
4.
Am
(maj7)
yes, those were the days. days.
C
D
Dm
A

80

TRAGEDY

Words & Music by Barry Gibb, Robin Gibb & Maurice Gibb

Moderately
Cm
Fm7
Cm
(Instrumental)
Gm/D
A♭/E♭
B♭/F
E♭/G
/A♭
/B♭
E♭
Here I lie in the lost and lone - ly part of town.
Night and day there's a burn - ing down in - side of me.
Held in time in a world of tears I slow - ly drown.
Burn - ing love with a yearn - ing that won't let me be.
F
G
Go - in' home I just can't make it all a - lone,
Down I go and I just can't take it all a - lone.
I real - ly should be

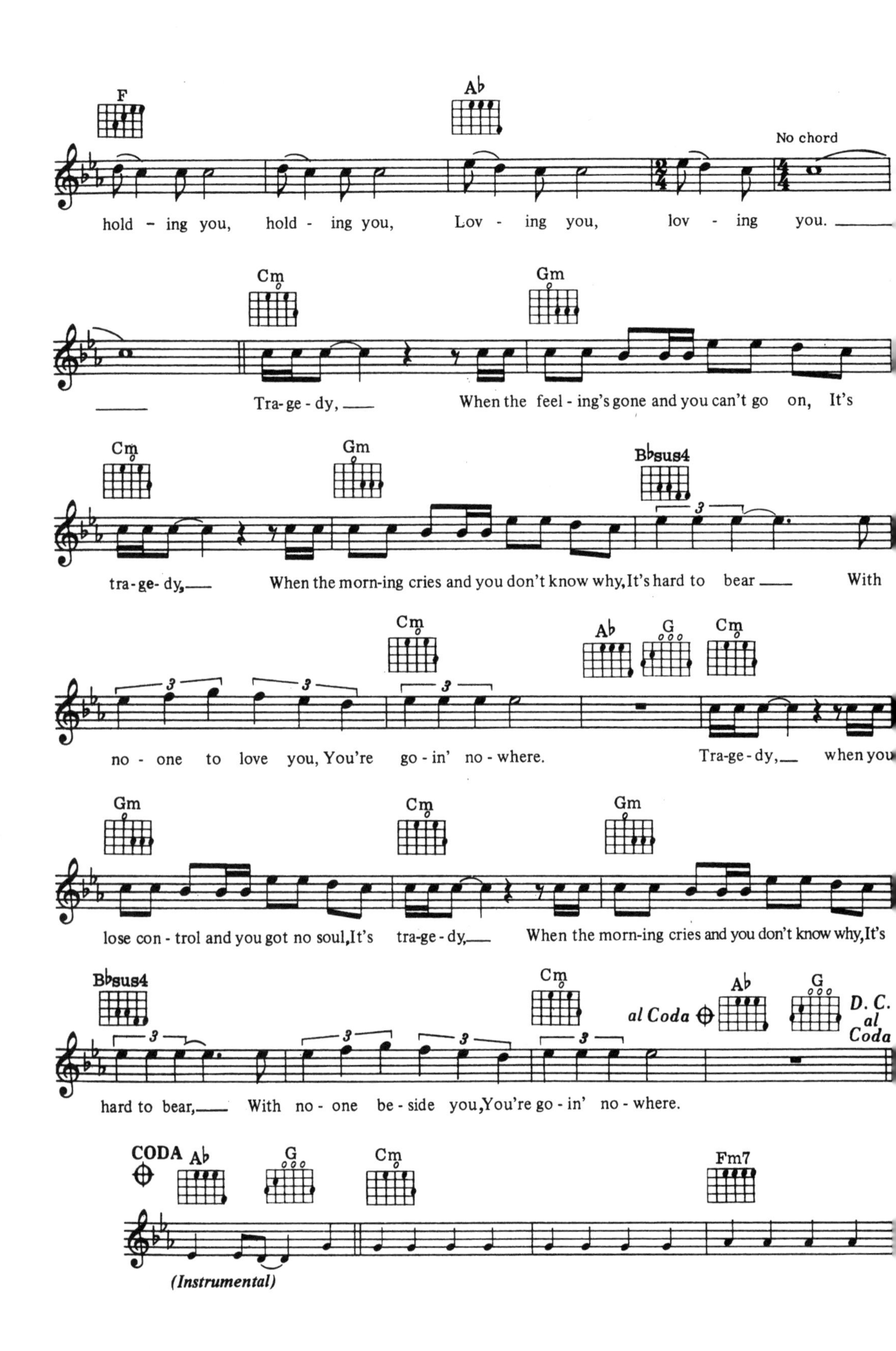
F
Ab
No chord
hold - ing you, hold - ing you, Lov - ing you, lov - ing you.
Cm
Gm
Tra-ge - dy, When the feel - ing's gone and you can't go on, It's
Cm
Gm
Bbsus4
tra-ge- dy, When the morn-ing cries and you don't know why, It's hard to bear With
Cm
Ab
G
Cm
no - one to love you, You're go - in' no - where. Tra-ge - dy, when you
Gm
Cm
Gm
lose con - trol and you got no soul, It's tra-ge - dy, When the morn-ing cries and you don't know why, It's
Bbsus4
Cm
al Coda
Ab
G
D. C. al Coda
hard to bear, With no - one be - side you, You're go - in' no - where.
CODA
Ab
G
Cm
Fm7
(Instrumental)

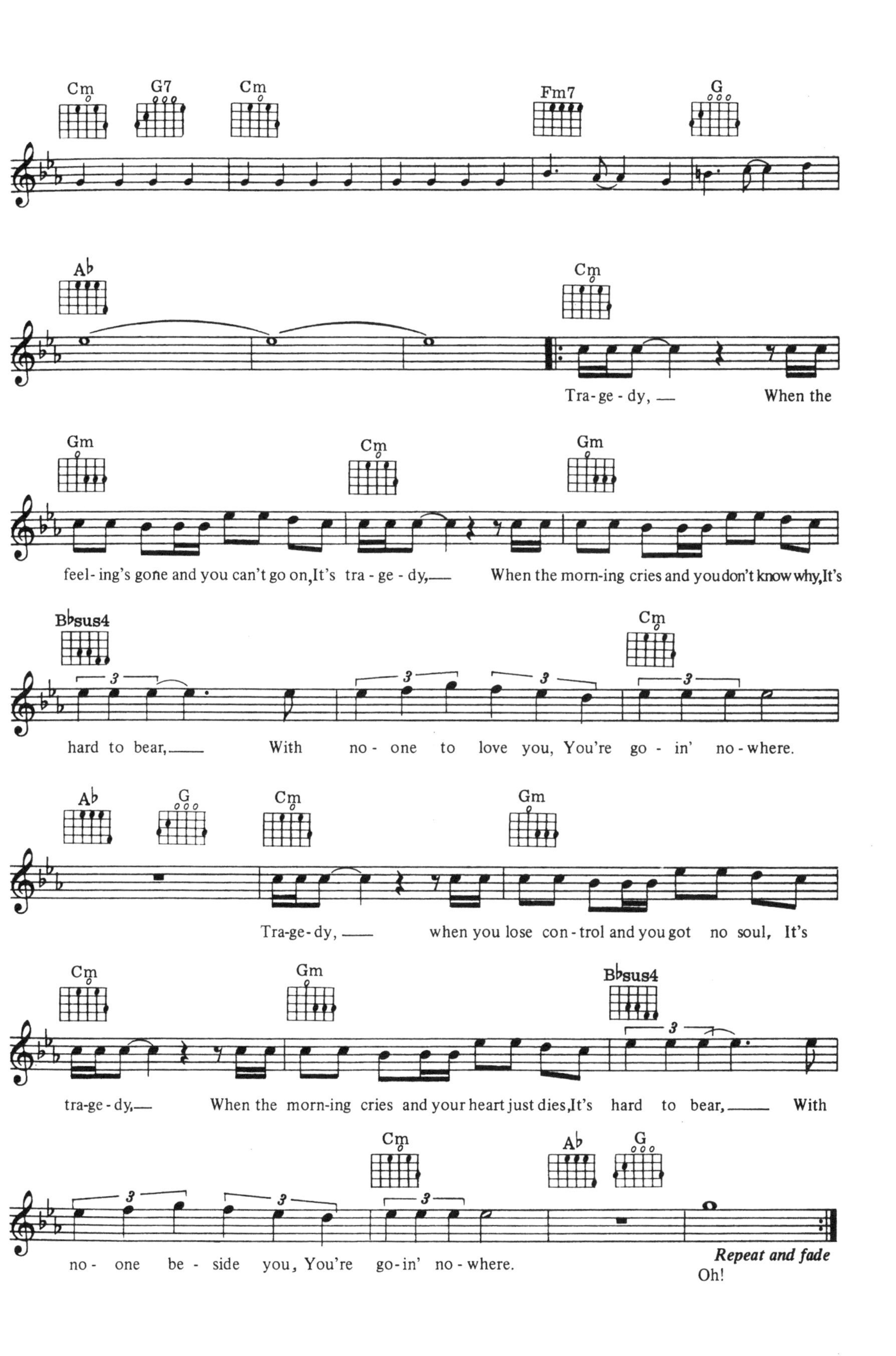
Cm
G7
Cm
Fm7
G
Ab
Cm
Tra-ge-dy, — When the
Gm
Cm
Gm
feel-ing's gone and you can't go on, It's tra-ge-dy, — When the morn-ing cries and you don't know why, It's
Bbsus4
Cm
hard to bear, — With no-one to love you, You're go-in' no-where.
Ab
G
Cm
Gm
Tra-ge-dy, — when you lose con-trol and you got no soul, It's
Cm
Gm
Bbsus4
tra-ge-dy, — When the morn-ing cries and your heart just dies, It's hard to bear, — With
Cm
Ab
G
no-one be-side you, You're go-in' no-where.
Repeat and fade
Oh!

TRUE

Words & Music by Gary Kemp

Moderato
G
Em7
Cmaj7
Bm
mf
Huh huh huh huh___ huh.__
Fmaj7
G
Bm
So true__ fun-ny how it seems_
With a thrill in my head___ and a pill on my_
C
E♭
G
al-ways in time,_ you__ nev - er in line for dreams._ Head o - ver heels
___ tongue dis-solve the nerves_ that have just be - gun._ List-'ning to Mar-
Bm
C
Em7
___ when toe to toe. This is the sound_________ of my soul,_
vin (all night long.)___ This is the sound_________ of my soul,_
Cmaj7
G
C
___ This is the sound.____ I bought a tick-et to the world_
___ This is the sound.____ Al - ways slip-ping from my hands._

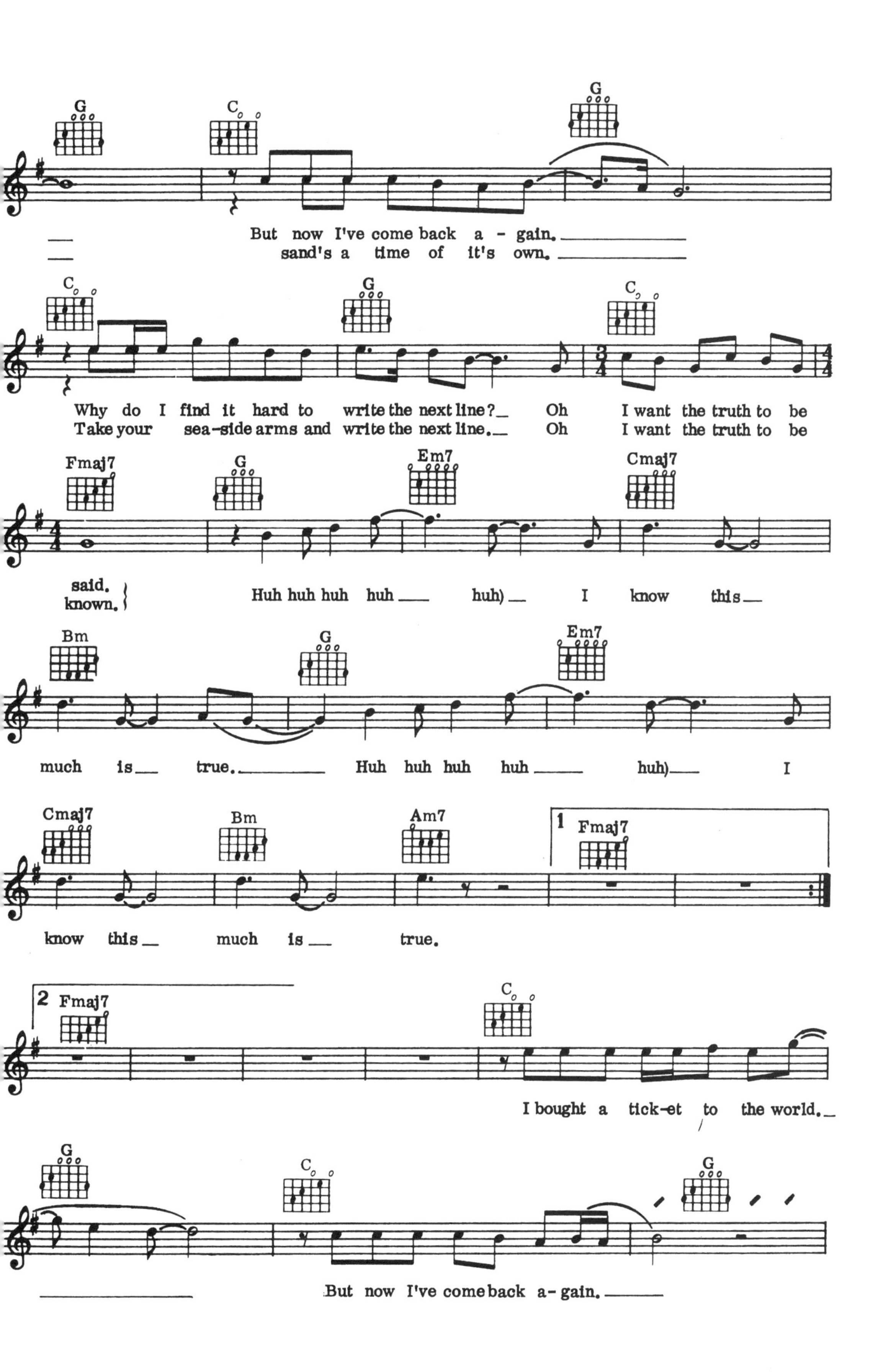
G
C
G
But now I've come back a - gain.
sand's a time of it's own.
C
G
C
3/4
4/4
Why do I find it hard to write the next line? Oh I want the truth to be
Take your sea-side arms and write the next line. Oh I want the truth to be
Fmaj7
G
Em7
Cmaj7
said.
known.
Huh huh huh huh huh) I know this
Bm
G
Em7
much is true. Huh huh huh huh huh) I
Cmaj7
Bm
Am7
1
Fmaj7
know this much is true.
2
Fmaj7
C
I bought a tick-et to the world.
G
C
G
But now I've come back a- gain.

C
G
C
Why do I find it hard to write the next line? Oh, I want the truth to be
Fmaj7
G
Em7
said. Huh huh huh huh huh, I
Cmaj7
Bm
G
know this much is true Huh huh huh huh
Em7
Cmaj7
Bm
Am7
huh, I know this much is true.
Em
Am7
Fmaj7
This much is true.
G
Em7
Cmaj7
Bm7
This much is true, this much is true. I know I know I know this much
G
Em7
Cmaj7
Bm7
Repeat & fade
true.
(This much is true, this much is true.)

UNCHAINED MELODY

Words by Hy Zaret
Music by Alex North

Moderato
G Em C
Oh, my love, my dar - ling, I've
D7 G Em D7
hun - gered for your touch a long lone - ly time.
G Em C
Time goes by so slow - ly, and
D7 G Em Bm
time can do so much, Are you still mine?
D7 G Em7
I need your love, I need your love,

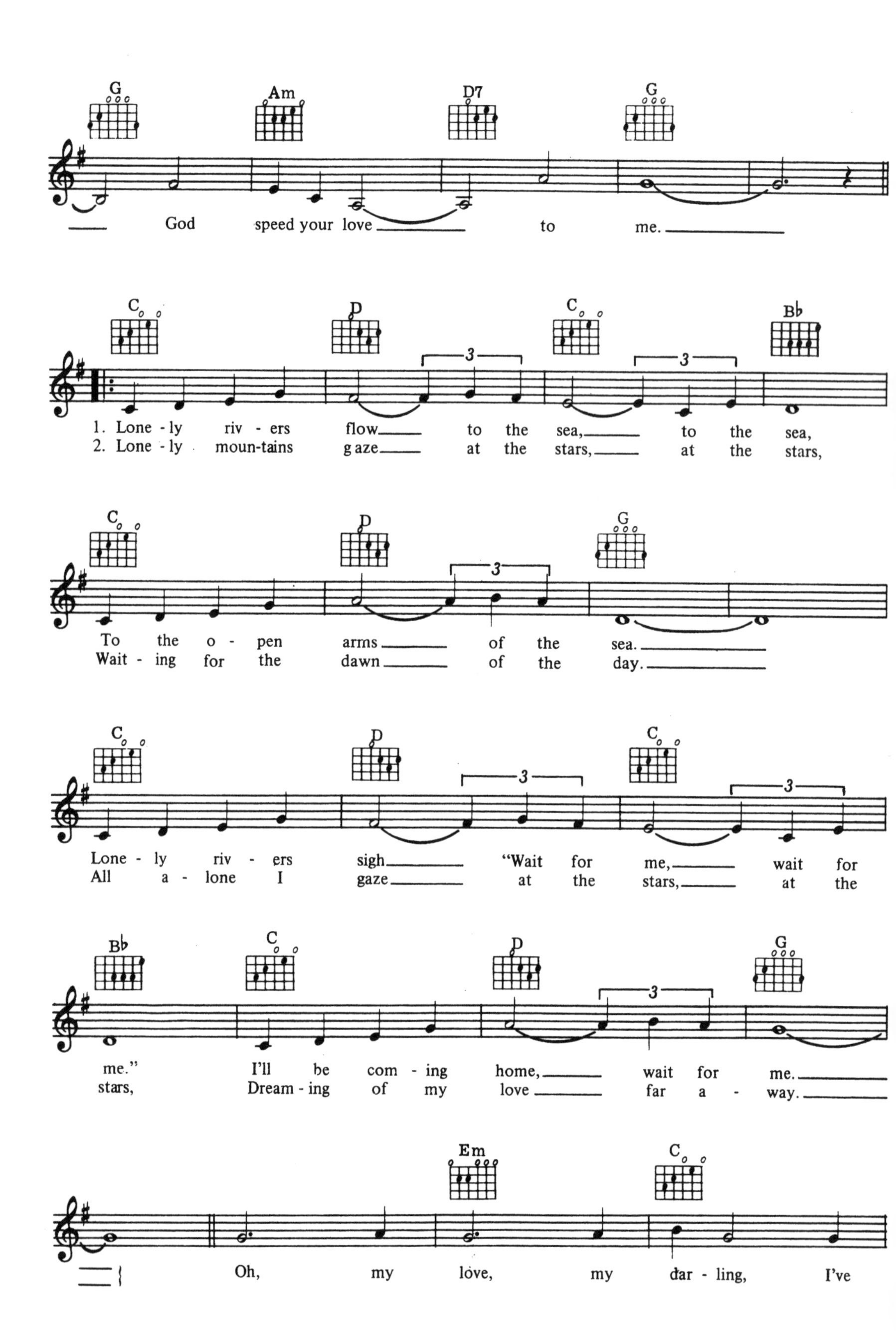
G
Am
D7
G
God speed your love to me.
C
D
C
B♭
1. Lone - ly riv - ers flow to the sea, to the sea,
2. Lone - ly moun-tains gaze at the stars, at the stars,
C
D
G
To the o - pen arms of the sea.
Wait - ing for the dawn of the day.
C
D
C
Lone - ly riv - ers sigh "Wait for me, wait for
All a - lone I gaze at the stars, at the
B♭
C
D
G
me." I'll be com - ing home, wait for me.
stars, Dream - ing of my love far a - way.
Em
C
Oh, my love, my dar - ling, I've

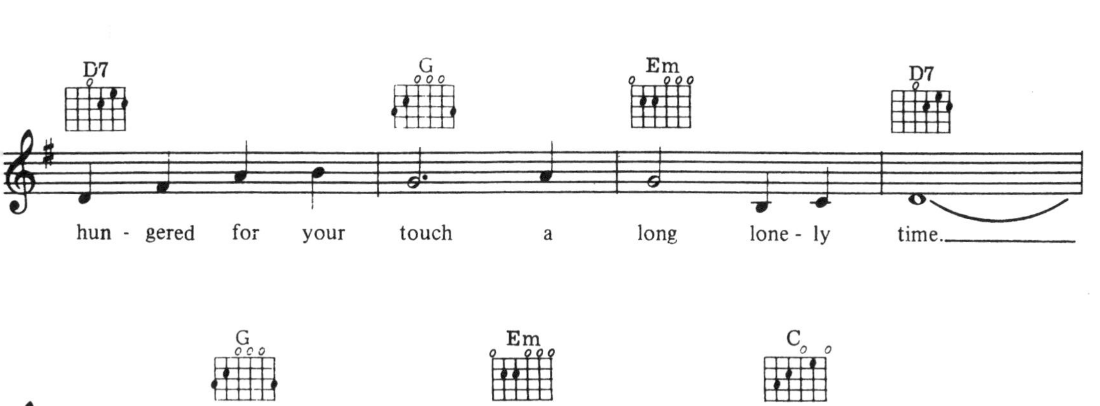
D7
G
Em
D7
hun - gered for your touch a long lone - ly time.

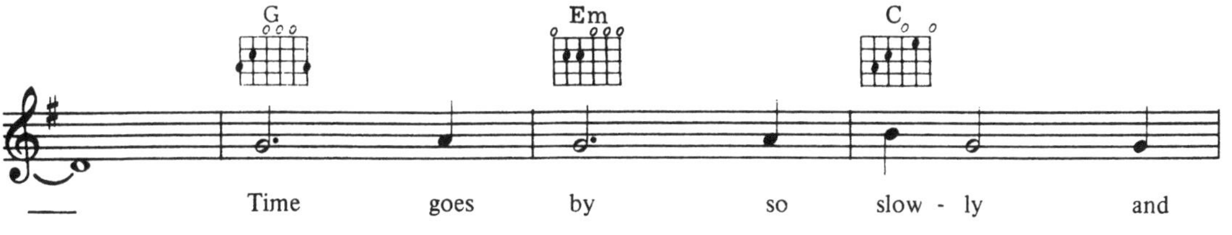
G
Em
C
Time goes by so slow - ly and

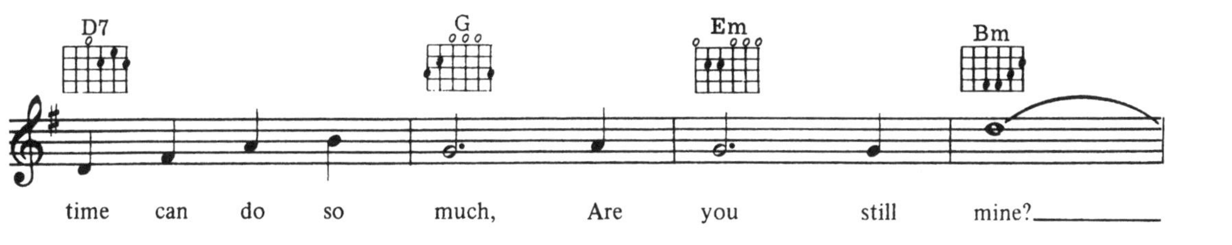
D7
G
Em
Bm
time can do so much, Are you still mine?

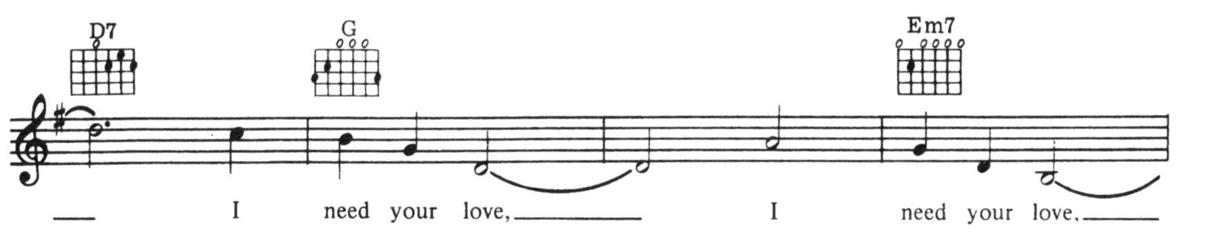
D7
G
Em7
I need your love, I need your love,

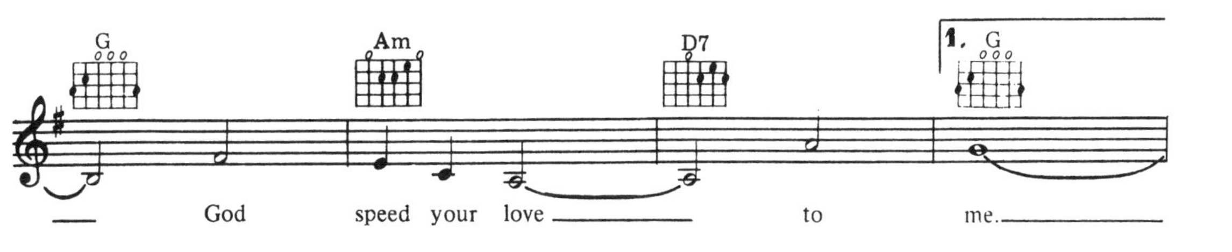
G
Am
D7
1. G
God speed your love to me.

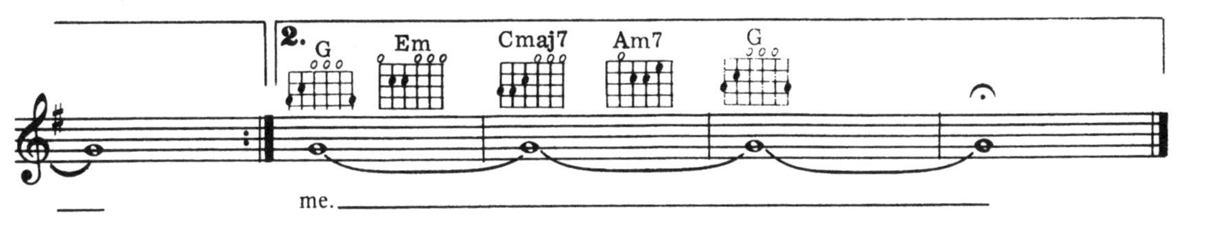
2. G
Em
Cmaj7
Am7
G
me.

83

VINCENT

Words & Music by Don McLean

Moderato

G
Star - ry, star-ry night, paint your pal - ette

Am
C
blue and grey, Look out on a summer's day, with

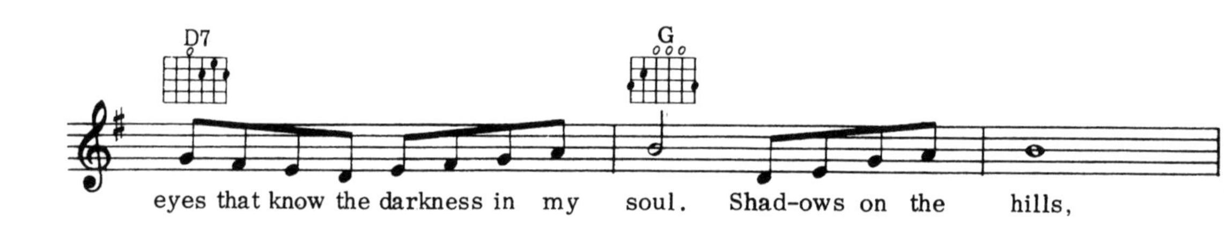
D7
G
eyes that know the darkness in my soul. Shad-ows on the hills,

Am
sketch the trees and the daf - fo-dils, Catch the breeze and the

C
D7
G
win-ter chills, In col-ours on the snow-y li-nen land. And now I un-der-

Am
D7
G
Em
stand what you tried to say to me, How you suf-fered for your

Am7
D7
Em
san-i-ty, How you tried to set them free. They would not lis-ten, they did

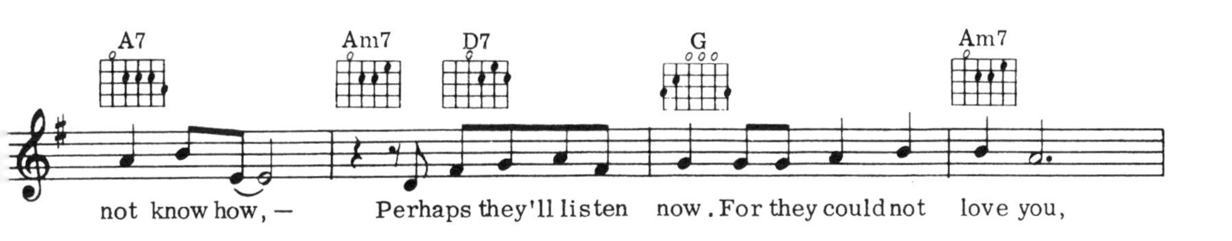
A7
Am7
D7
G
Am7
not know how, — Perhaps they'll listen now. For they could not love you,

D7
G
Em
Am7
But still your love was true, And when no hope was left in sight on that

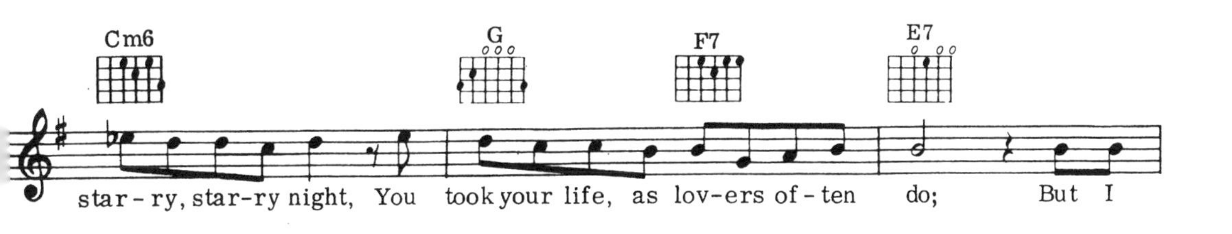
Cm6
G
F7
E7
star-ry, star-ry night, You took your life, as lov-ers of-ten do; But I

Am7
C
D7
G
could have told you, Vin-cent, This world was never meant for one as beau-ti-ful as you.

Walking On The Moon

Words & Music by Sting

Dm7add4
Dm7add4 Dm7 B♭/C C
(1,3) Gi-ant steps_ are what you take walk-ing on_ the moon._
(2) Walk-ing back_from your house walk-ing on_ the moon._
Dm7add4 Dm7 B♭/C C
I hope_ my legs don't break, walk-ing on_ the moon._
Walk-ing back from your house walk-ing on_ the moon._
Dm7add4 Dm7 B♭/C C
We could walk_ for ev - er, walk-ing on_ the moon._
Feet they hard - ly touch_ the ground,_ walk-ing on_ the moon._ My
Dm7add4 Dm7 B♭/C C
We could live_ to - geth - er walk-ing on,_ walk-ing on the moon
feet don't hard - ly make_ no sound,_ walk-ing on,_ walk-ing on the moon
Dm7add4

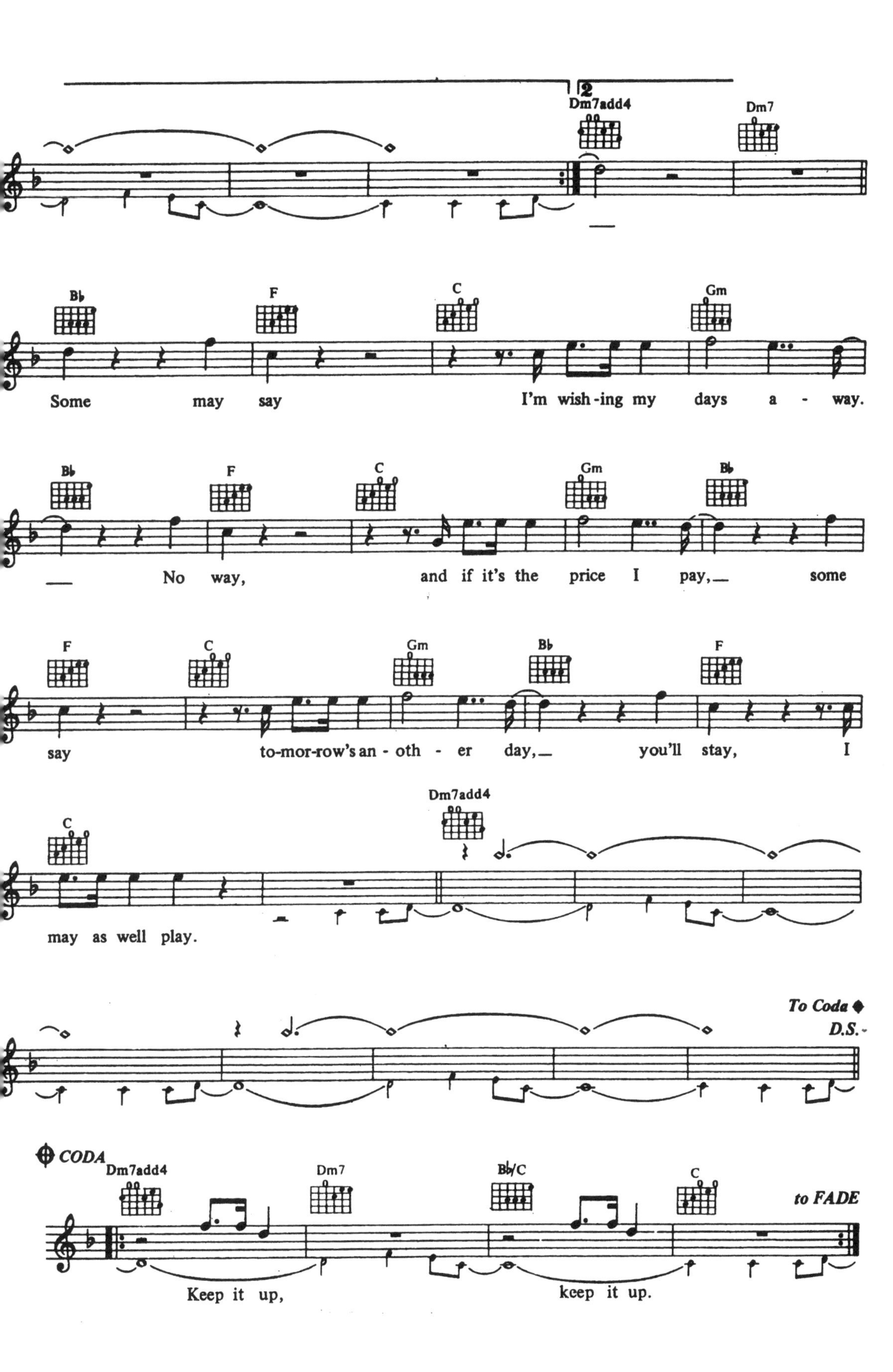
2
Dm7add4
Dm7
B♭
F
C
Gm
Some may say I'm wish-ing my days a - way.
No way, and if it's the price I pay, some
say to-mor-row's an - oth - er day, you'll stay, I
may as well play.
To Coda
D.S.
CODA
B♭/C
to FADE
Keep it up, keep it up.

85

WAY DOWN

Words & Music by Layng Martine, Jr.

Moderate Rock Tempo
C
Babe, you're get-ting clos - er, The lights are go - in' dim,
Ooh, my head is spin - nin', You got me in your spell,
The sound of your breath - in' has
A hun - dred ma - gic fin - gers on a
F7
made the mood I'm in.
whirl-ing car - ou - sel
All of my re - sis-
The med - i - cine with - in
Bb
F7
- tance ly - in' on the floor.
me, no doc - tor could pres - cribe.
Your
C
G7
Send - ing me to pla - ces I've nev-er been be-fore.
love is do - in' some - thing that I just can't des-cribe
C
Dm/C
tacet
G7
Ooh and I can feel it, feel it, feel
G7
CHORUS
it, feel it.
Way down where the mus-ic plays,

C
G7
Way down like a ti - dal wave, Way down where the fir-es blaze, Way
F
C
Dm/A
C/G
F
G7
down,
down,
way way on
C
1
2
down, (way on down)
down)
3
C
Hold me a - gain as tight
G7
as you can, I need you so, so ba - by let's go (way down) way down where it
C
G7
feels so good, Way down where I hoped it would, Way down where I
F
C
Dm/A
C/G
nev-er could, Way down
down
F
G7
C
Way, way on down. (way on down, way on down)

86
WE DON'T TALK ANYMORE

Words & Music by Alan Tarney

C
Am
1. Used to think that life was sweet, used to think we were so
to feel we had it made, used to feel we could sail
real-ly does-n't mat-ter to me, I guess your leav-ing was meant
Em7
F
Dm
com-plete. I can't be-lieve you'd throw it a-way.
a-way, Can you im-ag-ine how I feel to-day.
to be, It's down to you now, you want to be free.
C
F/C
1.
2.3.
2. Used
Well, it seems
Well, I hope
G
a long time a-go you were the lone-ly one,
you know which way to go you're on your own a-gain,
Now it comes to let-ting go you are the
Don't come cry-ing to me when you're the
G9
on-ly one, Do you know what you've done?
lone-ly one, Re-mem-ber what you've done?

CHORUS
G7
C
G/C
C
G/C
C
G/C
Dm/C
It's so fun - ny how we don't talk
an - y - more.
C
G/C
C
It's so fun - ny
G/C
C
G/C
Dm/C
why we don't talk an - y - more,
But I ain't los-ing sleep
C
Bb/C
F/C
Bb/C
F/C
and I ain't count - ing sheep.
C/G
G
G/A
D/A
A
E/A
A
E/A
A
E/A
Bm/A
It's so fun - ny how we don't talk
an-y - more.
(last time repeat to
chorus & fade adlib)
C
G/C
C
G/C
C
G/C
Dm/C
1
2
D.S.
3.Well, it

87

WELCOME HOME (VIVRE)

Original Words by Jean Dupre
Music by Stanislas Beldone
English Words by Bryan Blackburn

Moderately
F
C7
F
I'm so a - lone my love with - out you,
F7
Bb
C7
F
You're part of ev - 'ry - thing I do.
F7
Bb
C7
F
When you come back and you're be-
Dm
Gm7
C11
C7
F
- side me, These are the words I'll say to you.
CHORUS
F
Fmaj7
F7
Bb
Wel - come home, wel -
F
F7
Bb
F
C7
- come, Come on in and close the

F
Fmaj7
F7
B♭
F
F7
door, you've been gone too long
B♭
F
To Coda
C7
F
Wel - come you're home once more.
C7
F
I've thought of all the things I'll say to you,
There are so man - y lone - ly peo - ple,
F7
B♭
C9
C7
F
When you come back to me some day
Why must they ev - er be a - part.
F7
B♭
C7
F
When you are here, and we're to -
I hope some-day, you'll be to -
Dm
Gm
C11
C7
F
- geth - er,
- geth - er,
With all my love you'll hear me say,
Say - ing these words with all your heart,
D.S. al Coda
CODA
C7
F
You're home once more.

When The Going Gets Tough, The Tough Get Going

Words & Music by Wayne Brathwaite, Barry Eastmond, Robert John 'Mutt' Lange & Billy Ocean

Bounce tempo
G Em G
I got some-thing to tell you I got some-thing to
C G Em 1 G
say I'm gon-na put this dream in mo-tion ne-ver let no-thing stand in my
C G Em Dsus4 G Em
way. When the go-ing gets tough the tough get go-ing.
D 2 3 G C D Em
I'm gon-na love in the old fash-ioned way dar-ling I'll climb
G D Em C D
a-ny moun-tain dar-ling I'll do a-ny-thing Ooh!

G
Em
D
G
Ooh! can I touch you and do the things that lo - vers do
Em
D
G
Em
D
Ooh! Ooh! wan-na hold you I
G
Em
D
G
got to get it through to you, Ooh! when the go - ing gets tough the
Em
D
C
tough get go-ing; when the go - ing gets rough the tough get rough, Hey Hey Hey Hey Hey,
G
Em
D
G
Em
D
D. C.
D.S. ad lib. & fade
Em
D
I'm gon-na

VERSE 2:

I'm gonna get myself 'cross the river,
That's the price I'm willing to pay.
I'm gonna make you stand and deliver,
And give me love in the old fashioned way.

VERSE 3:

I'm gonna buy me a one way ticket,
Nothin's gonna hold me back,
Your love's like a slow train coming,
And I feel it coming down the track.

89

WHISPERING GRASS

Words by Fred Fisher
Music by Doris Fisher

Moderato
C
Em
F
Fm
Eb°
Dm7
G7+
C#°
G7
G13
Why do you whis - per, green grass? Why tell the trees what ain't so?
Whis - per - ing grass, the trees don't have to know, No, no.
Why tell them all your se - crets? Who kiss'd there long a - go?
Whis - per - ing grass, the trees don't need to know.

C G7 C Am F G7
Don't you tell it to the breeze 'cause she will tell the birds and bees and
C Am7 Dm7 G7
ev - 'ry - one will know be - cause you told the blab - ber - ing trees, Yes, you
3
Am E7-9 Am D7 Dm7 C#o
told them once be - fore; It's no se - cret an - y
Dm7 G7+ C Em
more. Why tell them all the old things?
F Fm C E♭o
They're bur - ied un - der the snow. Whis - per - ing grass, don't
Dm7 A♭7 Dm7 D♭maj7 C
tell the trees, 'cause the trees don't need to know.

UPTOWN GIRL

Words & Music by Billy Joel

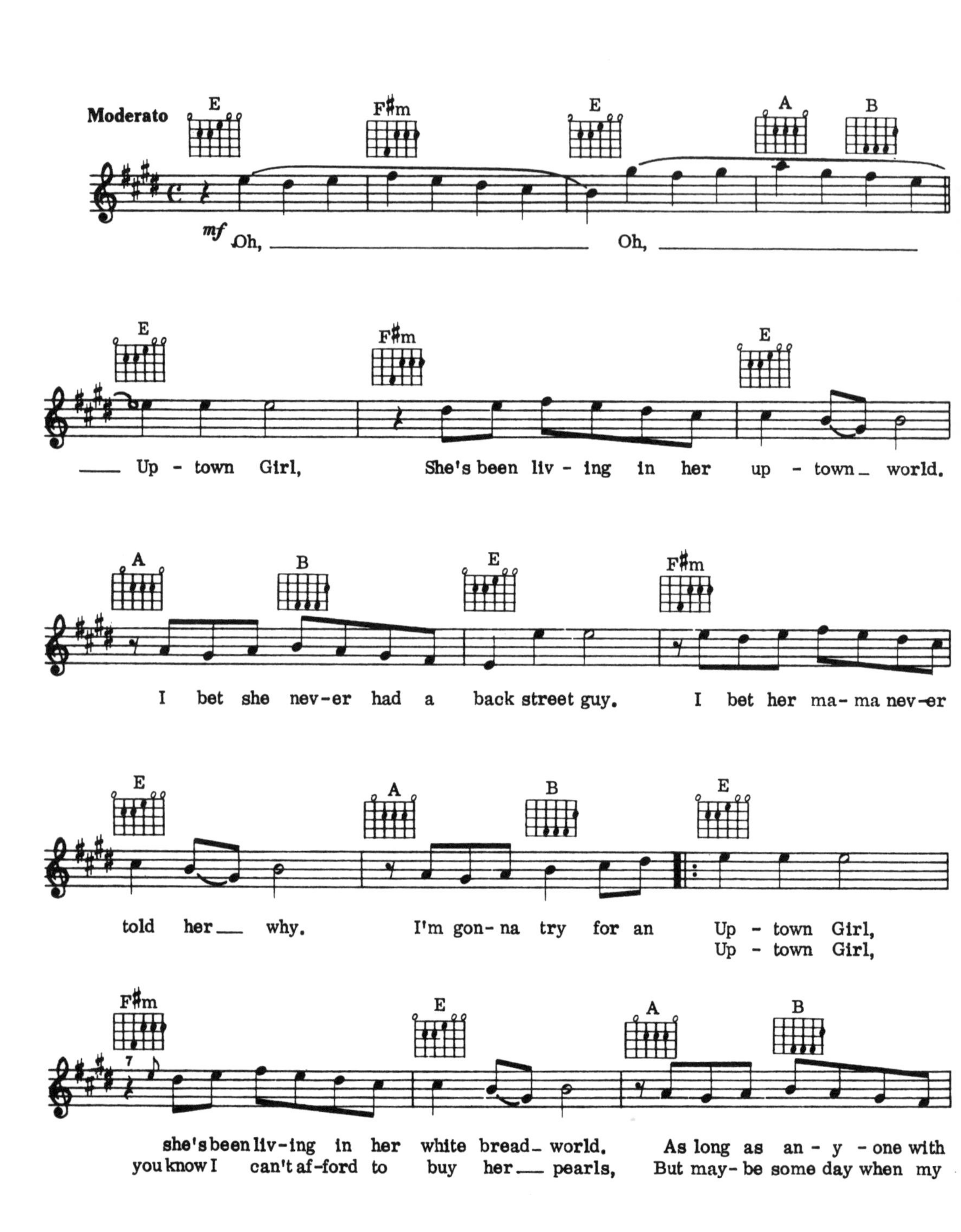
Moderato
E
F♯m
E
A
B
mf
Oh, ___ Oh, ___
___ Up - town Girl, She's been liv - ing in her up - town _ world.
I bet she nev-er had a back street guy. I bet her ma-ma nev-er
told her ___ why. I'm gon-na try for an Up - town Girl,
Up - town Girl,
she's been liv-ing in her white bread_ world. As long as an - y - one with
you know I can't af-ford to buy her ___ pearls, But may-be some day when my
7

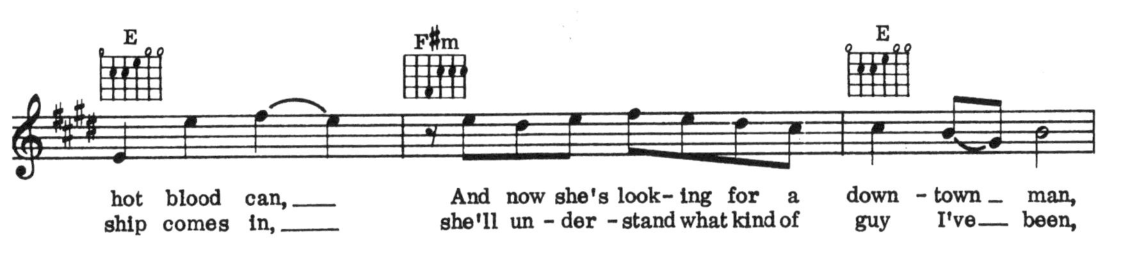
E
F♯m
E
hot blood can, And now she's look-ing for a down-town man,
ship comes in, she'll un-der-stand what kind of guy I've been,

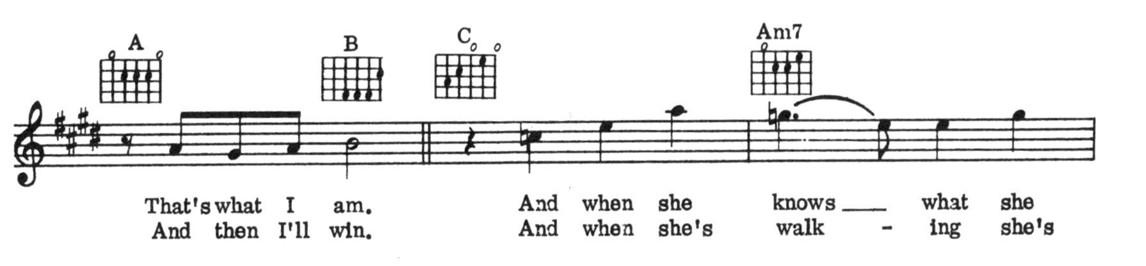
A
B
C
Am7
That's what I am. And when she knows what she
And then I'll win. And when she's walk-ing she's

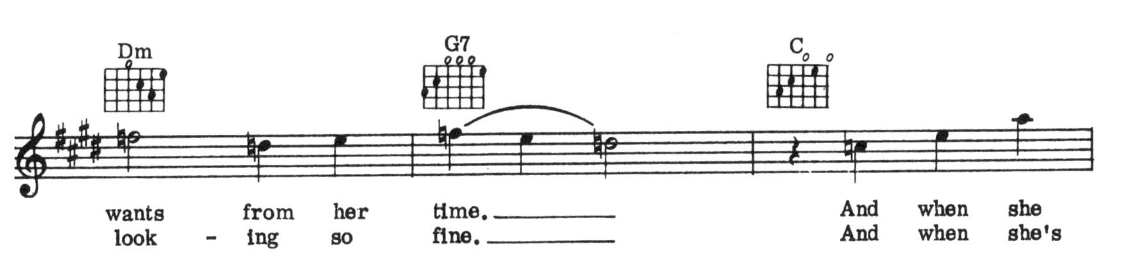
Dm
G7
C
wants from her time. And when she
look-ing so fine. And when she's

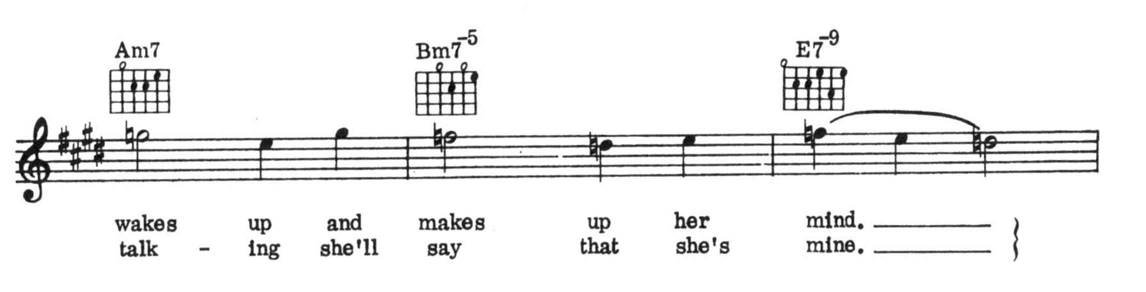
Am7
Bm7-5
E7-9
wakes up and makes up her mind.
talk-ing she'll say that she's mine.

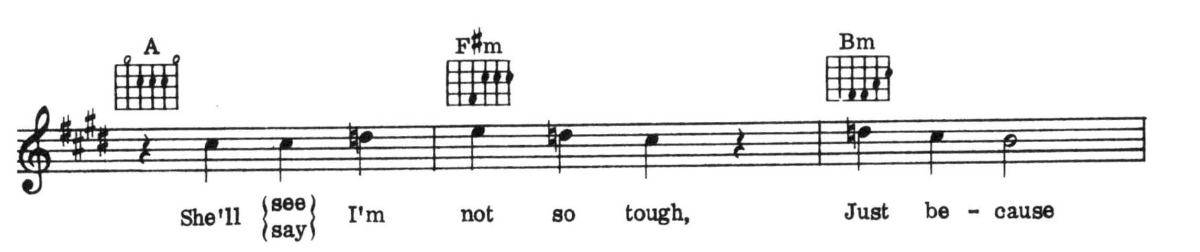
A
F♯m
Bm
She'll (see / say) I'm not so tough, Just be-cause

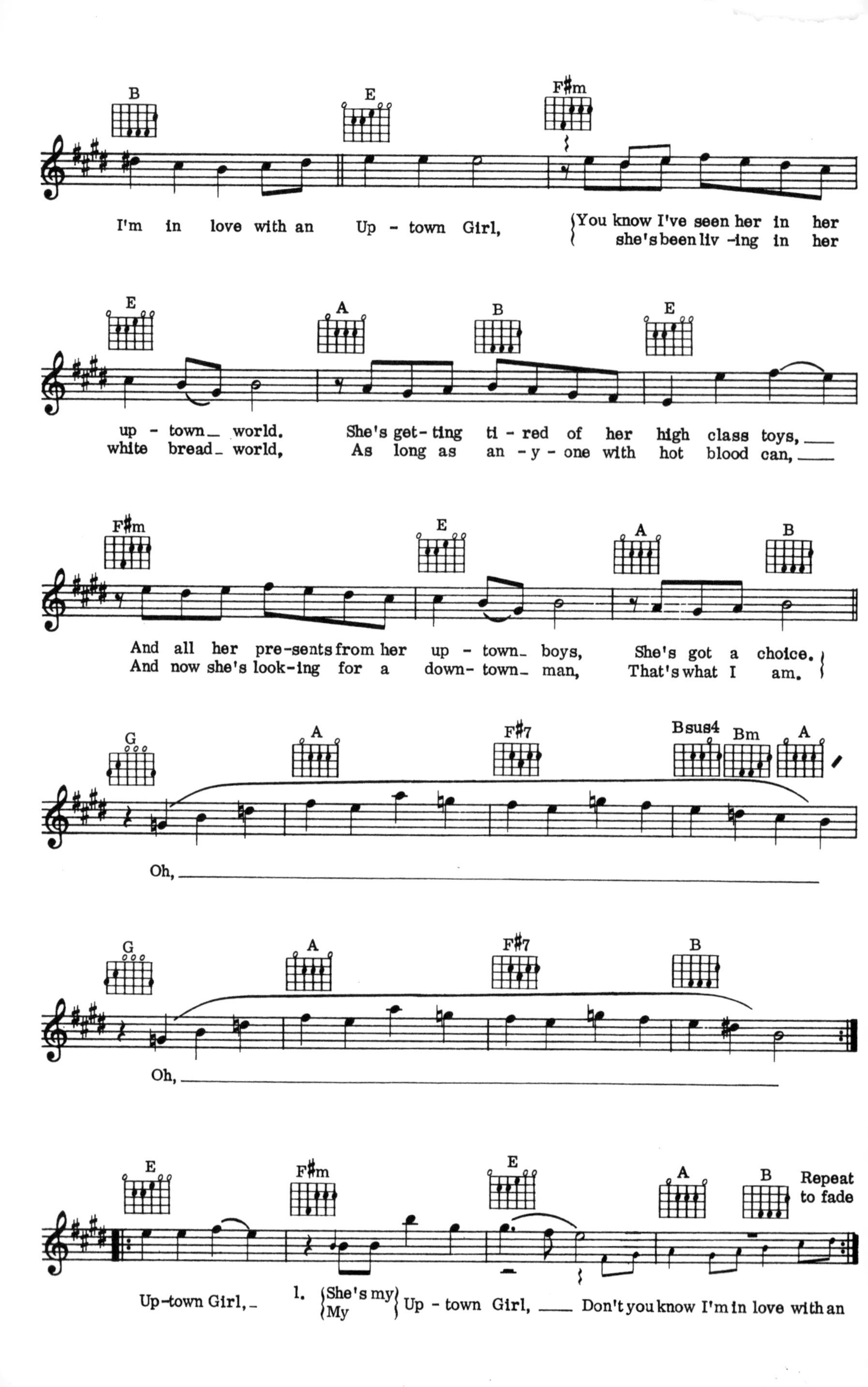
B
E
F#m
I'm in love with an Up - town Girl,
You know I've seen her in her up - town world.
she's been liv - ing in her white bread world,
E
A
B
E
She's get - ting ti - red of her high class toys,
As long as an - y - one with hot blood can,
F#m
E
A
B
And all her pre - sents from her up - town boys, She's got a choice.
And now she's look - ing for a down - town man, That's what I am.
G
A
F#7
Bsus4
Bm
A
Oh,
G
A
F#7
B
Oh,
E
F#m
E
A
B
Repeat to fade
Up - town Girl,
1. She's my
My
Up - town Girl, Don't you know I'm in love with an

A WHITER SHADE OF PALE

Words & Music by Keith Reid & Gary Brooker

Slowly
C Am F Dm G
Em G7 C F G
To Coda ⊕ (3rd. time)
F G7 C
We skipped the light fan-
She said there is no
Am F Dm7 G7
-dan-go and turned cart-wheels 'cross the floor I was feel-ing kind of
rea-son and the truth is plain to see But I wan-dered thro' my
Em Dm11 G7 C Am Em F
sea-sick but the crowd called out for more The room was hum-ming
play-ing cards and would not let her be One of six-teen vest - al
Dm7 G7 Em G7 C
hard-er as the ceil-ing flew a - way When we called out for an-
vir-gins who were leav-ing for the coast And al-though my eyes were
Am Em F Dm7 G13 C Cmaj7 Am
-oth - er drink the wait - er brought a tray And so it was that la - ter
o - pen they might just as well been closed
F Dm7 G7 Em Dm7 (on G)
as the mil-ler told his tale That her face at first just ghost-ly turned a
C F 1.2. C
whi - ter shade of pale.
⊕ CODA
C G7 (sus4) C(sus4) C

92
WITH A LITTLE HELP FROM MY FRIENDS

Words & Music by John Lennon & Paul McCartney

Moderato
E♭ Fm
What would you do if I sang out of tune; would you stand
What do I do when my love is a - way; [does it wor -
Would you be - lieve in a love at first-sight? Yes, I'm cer -
B♭7 E♭
up and walk out on me? Lend me your ears and I'll sing
- ry you to be a - lone?] How do I feel by the end
- tain that it hap-pens all the time. [What do you see when you turn
Fm B♭7
you a song, and I'll try not to sing out of key.
of the day; [are you sad be - cause you're on your own?]
out the light?] I can't tell you, but I know it's mine.
E♭ D♭ A♭ E♭
Oh / No / Oh I get by with a lit-tle help from my friends; mm, I get high
D♭ A♭ E♭
with a lit-tle help from my friends; mm, I'm gon-na try
A♭ 1 E♭ B♭7
with a lit-tle help from my friends.

2 & D.C.
E♭ Cm7 F7
[Do you need any-body?] I
E♭ D♭ A♭ Cm
need some-bo-dy to love. [Could it be any-bo-
F7 E♭ D♭ To Coda A♭
dy?] I want some-bo-dy to love.
D.C. al
CODA
A♭ D♭ A♭
Oh I get by with a lit-tle help from my friends;
E♭ D♭ A♭
mm, I'm gon-na try with a lit-tle help from my friends.
E♭ A♭
Oh I get high with a lit-tle help from my friends.
E♭ D♭
Yes, I get by with a lit-tle help from my friends,
A♭ C♭ A♭m6 E♭
with a lit-tle help from my friends.

93
WOMAN

Words & Music by John Lennon

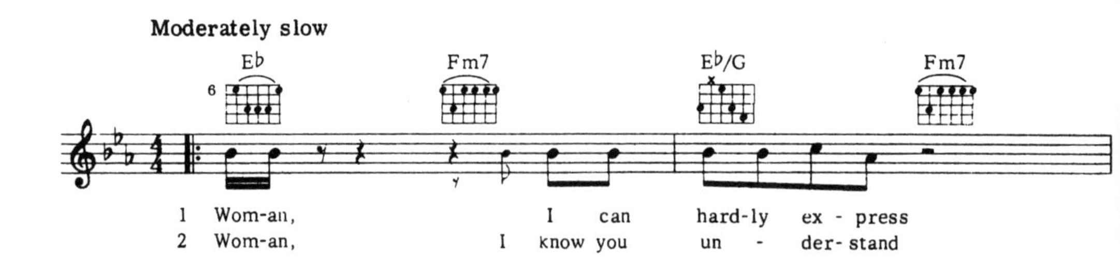
Moderately slow
Eb
Fm7
Eb/G
Fm7
1 Wom-an, I can hard-ly ex - press
2 Wom-an, I know you un - der- stand

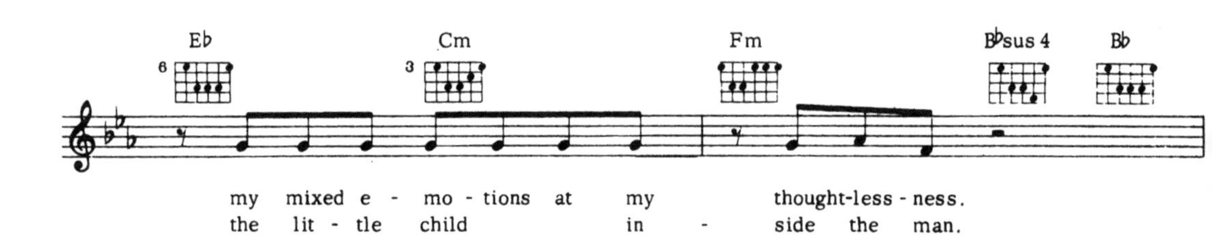
Eb
Cm
Fm
Bbsus 4
Bb
my mixed e - mo - tions at my thought-less - ness.
the lit - tle child in - side the man.

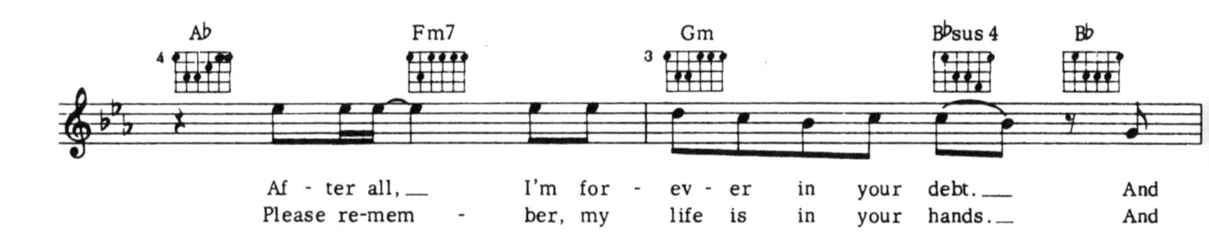
Ab
Fm7
Gm
Bbsus 4
Bb
Af - ter all, I'm for - ev - er in your debt. And
Please re-mem - ber, my life is in your hands. And

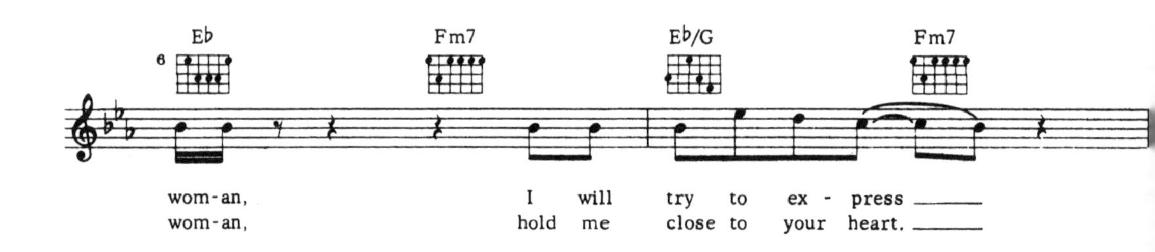
Eb
Fm7
Eb/G
Fm7
wom-an, I will try to ex - press
wom-an, hold me close to your heart.

Eb
Cm
Fm
Bbsus 4
Bb
my in - ner feel - ings and thank-ful - ness
How-ev - er dis - tant, don't keep us a - part.

Ab
Fm7
Gm
Bbsus 4
Bb
for show-ing me the mean-ing of suc - cess.
Af - ter all, it is writ-ten in the stars.
Ebma9
Cm7
Fm7
Bb6
Ebma9
Ooh, well, well, doo doo doo doo doo. Ooh,
Cm7
Fm7
1
Bb6
2
Bb6
well, well, doo doo doo doo doo. doo doo.
E
F#m7
E/G#
F#m7
Wom-an, please let me ex - plain.
E
C#m
F#m
Bsus 4
B
I nev - er meant to cause you sor-row or pain.
A
F#m7
G#m
Bsus 4
B
So let me tell you a - gain and a - gain and a - gain: I
Ema9
C#m7
F#m7
B6
(repeat to fade)
love you, yeah, yeah, now and for - ev-er. I

WITHOUT YOU

Words & Music by Peter Ham & Tom Evans

Slowly
Fmaj9 F6 Dm7
Well, I can't for - get this eve - ning and your face when you were leaving, But I
can't for - get to - mor-row when I think a - bout my sor-row. I
Gm7 A7+ A7
guess that's just the way the sto - ry goes. You al - ways
had you there, then I let you go. And now it's
Dm Dm/C B♭ B♭/A B♭/G F6 Fmaj9
smile, but in your eyes your sor-row shows, yes, it shows.
on - ly fair that I should let you know what you should know.
1 C9 C7 C9 C7
Well, I
2 C9 C7 C9 C7
I can't
CHORUS
F
live if
Dm Gm
liv-ing is with-out you, I can't live, I can't
C9 C7 F Dm
live an - y - more. I can't live if liv-ing is with-out you. I can't
Gm 1 C9 C7 D.S. (with rpt) 2 C9 C7 Rpt. Chos. and fade.
live, I can't live an- y-more, But I live an- y - more. I can't

95
A Woman In Love

Words & Music by Barry Gibb & Robin Gibb

G
Am
B7
but I give you it all.
but I give you it all.
Em
B
Em
B
I am a wo - man in love
and I'd do an - y - thing
Em
B
Em
B
to get you in - to my world,
and hold you with - in.
Em
D
Am
It's a right
I de - fend
G
To Coda
Em
o - ver and o - ver a - gain.
What do I do?
C
D.C. (Vs.2) al Coda
CODA
Em
B
What do I do?
I am a wo - man in love
Em
B
Em
B
and I'm talk - in' to you.
I know how you feel,

Em
B
Em
what a wo - man can do.
It's a
D
Am
right
I de - fend
B7
o - ver and o - ver a - gain.
Em
B
Em
B
I am a wo - man in love,
and I'd do an - y - thing
Em
B
Em
B
to get you in - to my world,
and hold you with - in.
Em
D
It's a right
I de -
Am
- fend
o - ver and o - ver a -
1
B
- gain.
2
B
Em
- gain.

WOODEN HEART

Words & Music by Fred Wise, Ben Weisman, Kay Twomey & Bert Kaempfert

Moderately (in 2)
E♭
Fm7
B♭7
Can't you see I love you, Please don't
E♭
A♭
E♭
break my heart in two, That's not hard to
Fm7
B♭7
do, 'Cause I don't have a wood - en
E♭
Fm7
B♭7
E♭
heart. And if you say "Good -
Fm7
B♭7
E♭
A♭
E♭
- bye," Then I know that I would cry,
A♭
E♭
Fm7
May - be I would die 'Cause I don't have a

B♭7
E♭
A♭
E♭
wood - en heart.
There's no
Fm7
B♭7
E♭
strings up - on this love of
A♭
mine, It was al - ways you from the
E♭
E°
B♭7
E♭
start.
Treat me nice, treat me
Fm7
B♭7
E♭
A♭
E♭
good, Treat me like you real - ly should, 'Cause
A♭
E♭
Fm7
I'm not made of wood, And I don't have a
B♭7
E♭
A♭
E♭
wood - en heart.

Words

Words & Music by Barry Gibb, Robin Gibb & Maurice Gibb

Moderato
No chord
G
Smile an ev - er - last - ing smile; a smile could bring you
A
near to me.
D
Don't ev - er let me find you
C
G
gone 'cause that would bring a tear to me. This
B♭
world has lost its glo - ry; let's start a brand - new sto - ry
F
now, my love.
G
Right now, there'll be no oth - er
A
D
time, and I can show you how, my love.

G
A
Talk in ev - er - last - ing words and ded - i - cate them all to me.
D
And I will give you all my life, I'm here if you should
C
G
B♭
call to me. You think that I don't e - ven
D
Tacet
mean a sin - gle word I say. It's on - ly
G
D
words, and words are all I have to take your heart a -
G
D
Tacet
G
way. It's on - ly words, and words are all I
D
G
D
Tacet
have to take your heart a - way. It's on - ly
G
words, and words are all I have to take your heart a - way.

THE WONDER OF YOU

Words & Music by Baker Knight

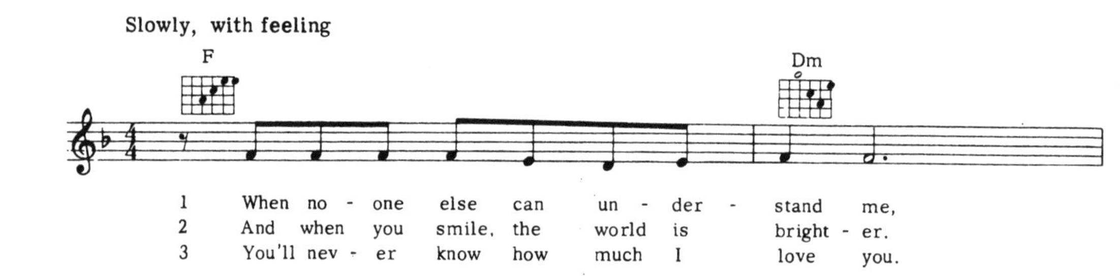
Slowly, with feeling
F
Dm
1 When no - one else can un - der - stand me,
2 And when you smile, the world is bright - er.
3 You'll nev - er know how much I love you.

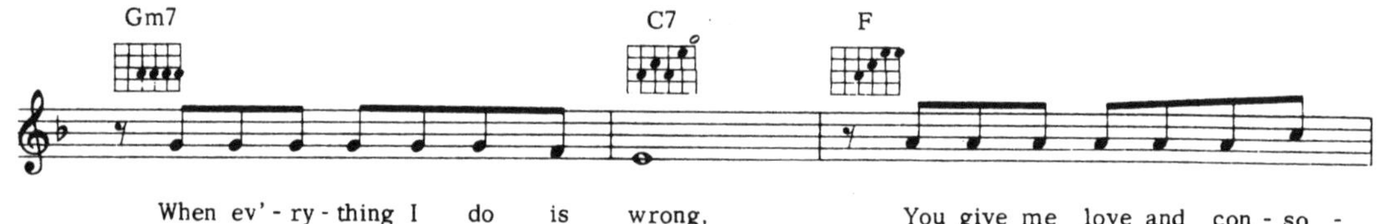
Gm7
C7
F
When ev' - ry - thing I do is wrong,
You touch my hand and I'm a king.
My love is yours and yours a - lone,
You give me love and con - so -
Your kiss to me is worth a
And it's so won - der - ful to

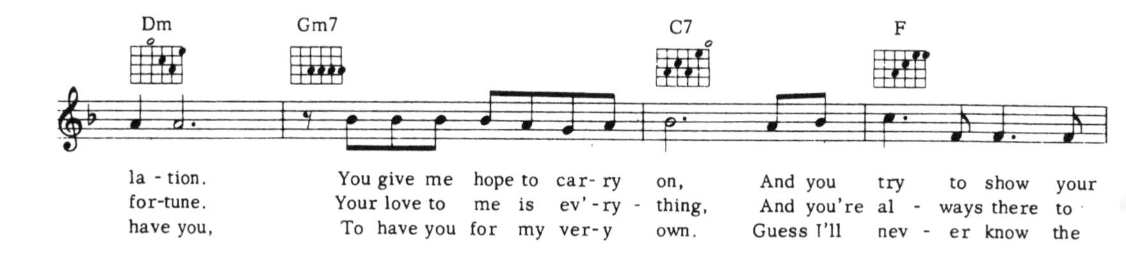
Dm
Gm7
C7
F
la - tion. You give me hope to car - ry on, And you try to show your
for - tune. Your love to me is ev' - ry - thing, And you're al - ways there to
have you, To have you for my ver - y own. Guess I'll nev - er know the

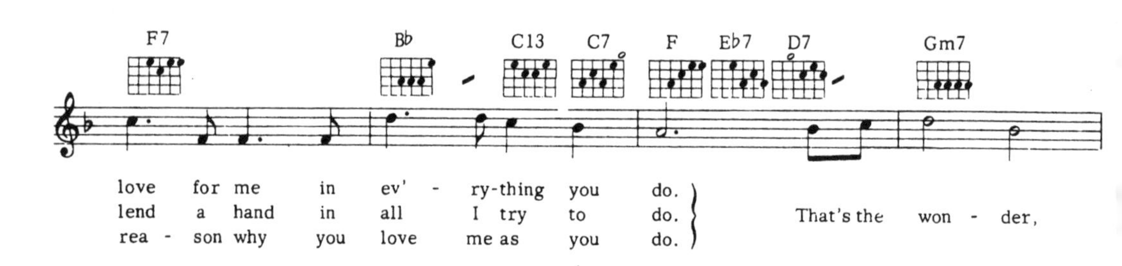
F7
B♭
C13
C7
F
E♭7
D7
Gm7
love for me in ev' - ry - thing you do.
lend a hand in all I try to do.
rea - son why you love me as you do.
That's the won - der,

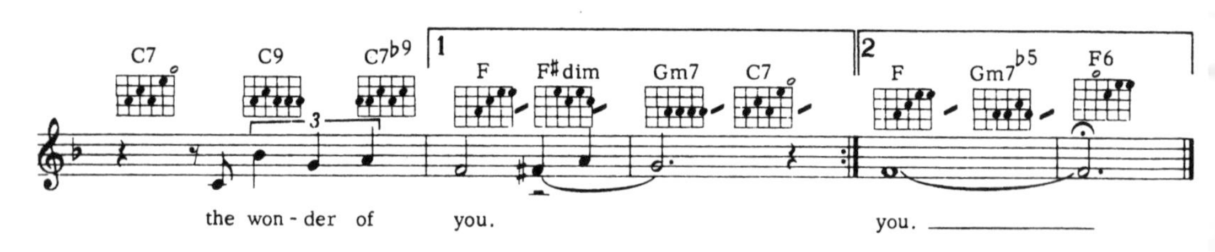
C7
C9
C7♭9
1
F
F♯dim
Gm7
C7
2
F
Gm7♭5
F6
the won - der of you.
you.

99
Y.M.C.A.

Words & Music by Jacques Morali, Henri Belolo & Victor Willis

Lively Beat
F
Young man, there's no need to feel down. I said
Young man, I was once in your shoes. I said
Dm
Bb
young man pick your-self off the ground. I said Young man 'cause you're
I was down and out with the blues. I felt no man cared if
C
Bb
Am
Gm
Am
C7
in a new town there's no need to— be —— un - hap - py
I were a - live, I felt the whole— world —— was so jive.
F
Dm
Young man, there's a place you can go. I said young man, when you're
That's when some - one came up to me and said "Young man, take a
Bb
short on your dough you can stay there, and I'm sure you will find man-y
walk up the street, it's a place there, called the Y. M. C. A. They can
C
Bb
Am
Gm
Am
C7
ways to— have —— a good time.
start you— back —— on your way."
tacet
F
It's fun to stay at the Y. M. C. A. it's fun to stay at the

Dm
Gm7
Y. M. C. A.—— They have ev-ery - thing—for young
al Coda
C11
men to en - joy, you can hang out with all—— the boys.—
F
It's fun to stay at the Y. M. C. A. It's fun to stay at the
Dm
Gm7
Y. M. C. A. You can get yourself clean, you can
C11
C7
have a good meal, you can do what-ev-er —— you feel.——
F
Young man, are you list-'ning to me? I said
No man does it all by him - self, I said
Dm
B♭
young man, what do you want to be? I said young man, you can
young man, put your pride on the shelf and just go there to the
C
B♭
Am
Gm
Am
C7
make real your dreams, but you've got to— know —— this one thing.
Y. M. C. A. I'm sure they can— help —— you to - day.

F
It's fun to stay at the Y. M. C. A.
Y. M. C. A.
Dm
It's fun to stay at the Y. M. C. A. They have
It's fun to stay at the Y. M. C. A. You can
Gm7
1. C11
ev-'ry-thing— for young men to en-joy, you can hang out with all—the boys.—
get yourself clean,—you can have a good meal, you can
2. C11
D. S. al Coda
It's fun to stay at the do what-ev-er— you feel.
CODA C11
F
hang out with all— the boys.
Y. M. C. A.
Y. M. C. A.
Dm
It's fun to stay at the Y. M. C.A.
Yes, just go— to the Y. M. C.A.
Gm7
Young man, young man, there's no need to feel down,
Young man, young man, I was once in your shoes,
C11
Repeat & fade ad lib
3
Young man, young man, get your - self off the ground.
Young man, young man, I was down with the blues.

100

Young At Heart

Words & Music by Robert Hodgens, Siobhan Fahey & Bobby Valentino

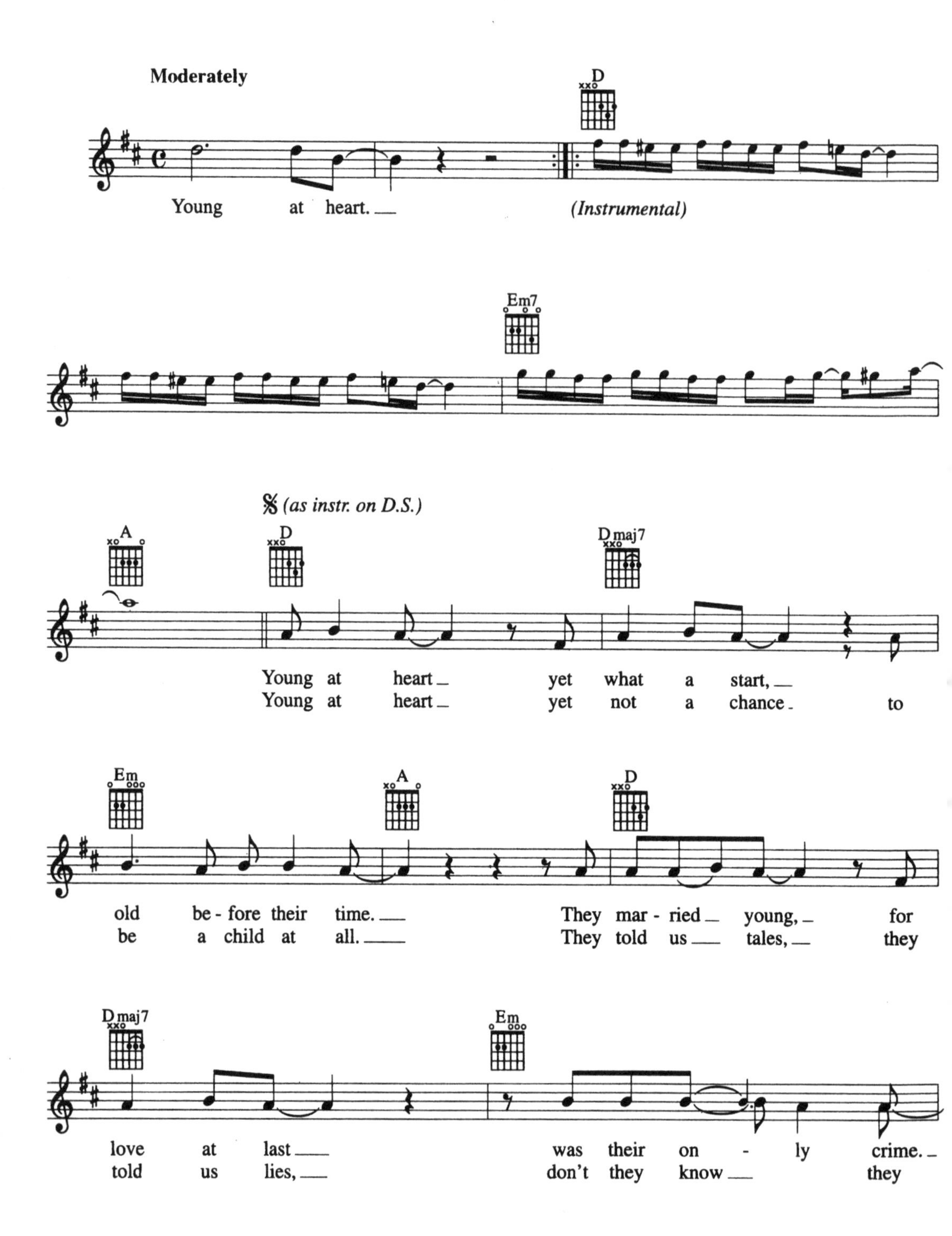
Moderately
D
Young at heart.
(Instrumental)
Em7
A
𝄋 (as instr. on D.S.)
D
Dmaj7
Young at heart yet what a start,
Young at heart yet not a chance to
Em
A
D
old be - fore their time.
be a child at all.
They mar - ried young, for
They told us tales, they
Dmaj7
Em
love at last was their on - ly crime.
told us lies, don't they know they

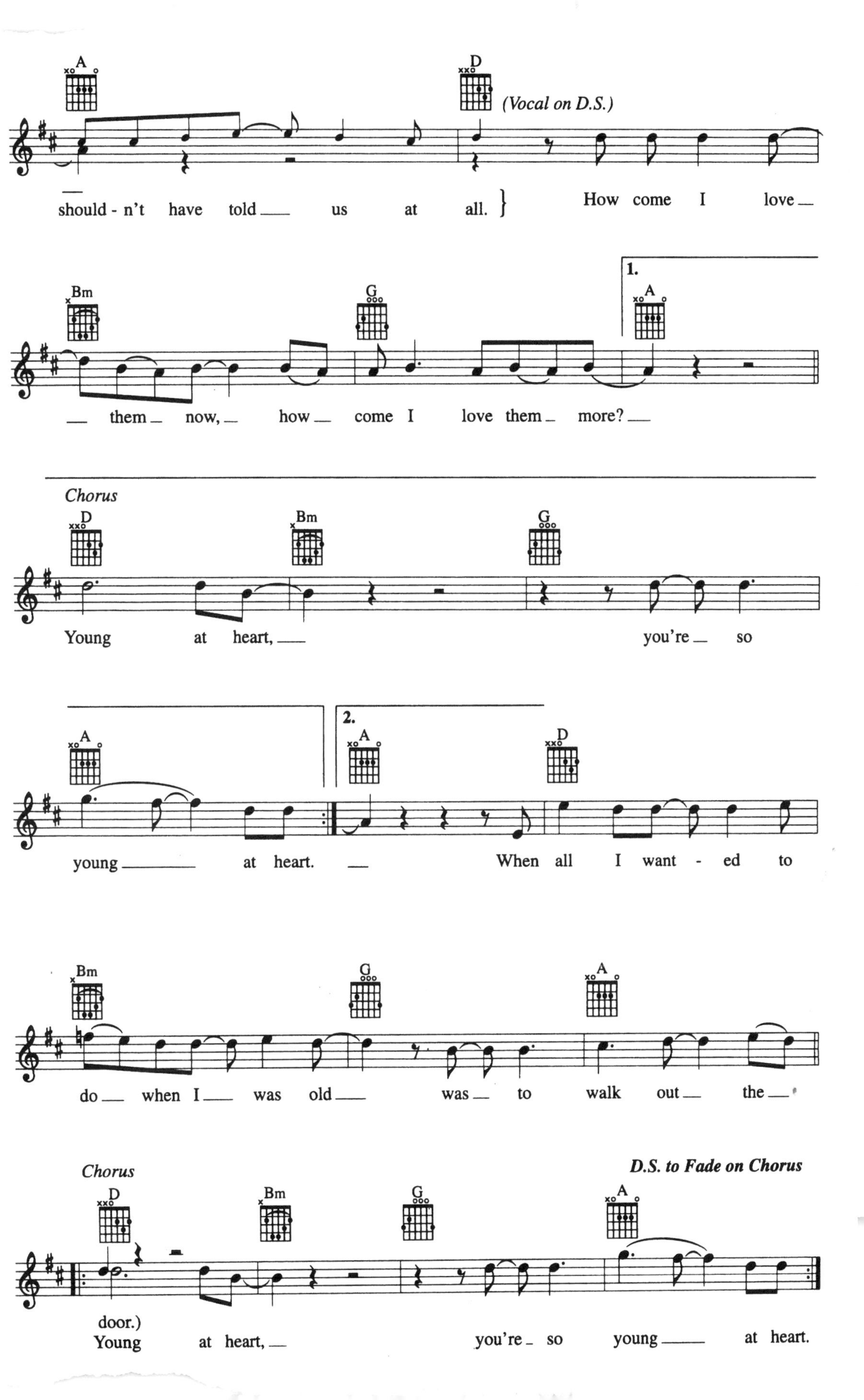
A
D
(Vocal on D.S.)
should - n't have told us at all. }
How come I love
Bm
G
1.
A
them now, how come I love them more?
Chorus
D
Bm
G
Young at heart, you're so
2.
A
A
D
young at heart.
When all I want - ed to
Bm
G
A
do when I was old was to walk out the
Chorus
D.S. to Fade on Chorus
D
Bm
G
A
door.)
Young at heart, you're so young at heart.

YELLOW SUBMARINE

Words & Music by John Lennon & Paul McCartney

March tempo
D C G Em7 Am C
1. In the town where I was born lived a man who sailed to
2. sailed up to the sun till we found the sea of
D G D C G Em7 Am C
sea, And he told us of his life in the land of sub-ma-
green, And we lived be-neath the waves in our yel- low sub-ma-
1 D G 2 D G D
-rines. 2. So we -rine. We all live in a yel-low sub-ma-rine,
G
yel - low sub - ma-rine, yel - low sub- ma - rine, We all live in a
D G
yel - low sub - ma-rine, yel - low sub-ma - rine, yel-low sub- ma-rine, And our
As we
D C G Em7 Am C
friends are all on board, ma - ny more of them live next
live a life of ease, ev - 'ry one of us has all we
D G D C 1 G 2 G D.S. and Fade
door. And the band be-gins to play. green.
need. Sky of blue and sea of

6/15(194217)